ANIMAL INTELLIGENCE

ANIMAL INTELLIGENCE

EXPERIMENTAL STUDIES

BY

EDWARD L. THORNDIKE
TEACHERS COLLEGE, COLUMBIA UNIVERSITY

(fascimile of 1911 edition)

HAFNER PUBLISHING COMPANY
New York and London
1965

Originally published 1911

Reprinted 1965

Printed and Published by
Hafner Publishing Company, Inc.
31 East 10th Street
New York, N.Y. 10003

Printed in U.S.A. by
NOBLE OFFSET PRINTERS, INC.
NEW YORK 3, N. Y.

INTRODUCTION TO THE 1965 RE-PRINT

In his preface, Professor Thorndyke wrote in January, 1911, that "the main purpose of this volume is to make accessible to students of psychology and biology the author's experimental studies of animal intellect and behavior." These studies then were incorporated as they were written originally, the earliest appearing in 1898. At the turn of the century considerable interest was already manifest among many investigators of behavior, especially that which could be related to the brain. The Herrick brothers (Clarence L. and C. Judson) had established the *Journal of Comparative Neurology and Psychology* (1891). Robert Yerkes was actively engaged in an experimental approach to psychology, eventually writing two books of considerable significance related to intelligence, namely, *The Great Apes* (1929) and *Chimpanzees* (1943). C. Judson Herrick's *Neurological Foundations of Animal Behavior* (1924) paved the way for much more concern for behavior in its relation to the nervous system. Karl S. Lashley's *Brain Mechanisms and Intelligence* (1929) gave emphasis to a point of view by which the experimentalist could attack the problem of the nature of intelligence and learning as these are related to the brain. At that time he frankly admitted that "the whole theory of learning and intelligence is in confusion. We know at present nothing of the organic basis of these functions and little enough of either the variety or uniformities of their expression in behavior." If this was true for Lashley in 1929, it was even more so for Thorndyke in 1911. Yet his *Animal Intelligence* was a major milestone in the course of experimental psychology and behavior. C. Lloyd Morgan's *Animal Behavior* (1900) should also be considered one of these milestones in this slow process of understanding behavior. Jenning's book *Behavior of the Lower Organisms* (1906) was fundamental in this attack upon these problems. C. Judson Herrick's essay, *The Evolution of Intelligence and its Organs* published one year before Thorndyke's *Animal Intelligence* set the stage upon which recent generations of behavioral scientists have approached their tasks with more refined techniques, yet with considerable confusion and uncertainty.

Scientists of the present era in animal behavior (intelligence), have produced a plethora of papers, books and symposia. Most of these studies have more or less related their findings as well as they could to brain function. This, however, is not necessarily true of such ethologists as Tinbergen or Lorenz.

As examples of the present concern with problems of intelligence (behavior-learning) we can sight only a few of the major works. Mary A. B. Brazier's editing of the three volumes on *The Central Nervous System and Behavior* by the Josiah Macy Foundation in conjunction with the National Science Foundation, and Dr. Brazier's editorship of the series, *Brain and Behavior* sponsored by the American Institute of Biological Sciences and the National Science Foundation.

Harlow & Woolsey's *Biological and Biochemical Bases of Behavior* is an outstanding example of the modern approach to major problems confronting behavioral scientists who, through the technique of symposia, work at the interdisciplinary level.

Thorndyke's *Animal Intelligence* is one of the first major contributions to the problems of learning. It is well that we have readily available these classical experimental designs for in their simplicity they asked fundamental questions of nature, the answers to which we still are earnestly seeking as brought out for example, in the sophisticated approaches in the symposium *Neurological Basis of Behavior* edited by G. E. W. Wolstenholme and Cecelia M. O'Connor.

Animal Intelligence is a universal fascinating subject. It concerned Aristotle and it concerns all modern students of behavior, whether they work at the molecular level or in the field as George Schaller so ably has in his gorilla studies in the African rain forests. Thorndyke's contributions were major links in this ever-intriguing, on-going problem of behavior.

Paul G. Roofe
The University of Kansas
Lawrence, Kansas

March 22, 1965

PREFACE

THE main purpose of this volume is to make accessible to students of psychology and biology the author's experimental studies of animal intellect and behavior.[1] These studies have, I am informed by teachers of comparative psychology, a twofold interest. Since they represent the first deliberate and extended application of the experimental method in animal psychology, they are a useful introduction to the later literature of that subject. They mark the change from books of general argumentation on the basis of common experience interpreted in terms of the faculty psychology, to monographs reporting detailed and often highly technical experiments interpreted in terms of original and acquired connections between situation and response. Since they represent the point of view and the method of present animal psychology, but in the case of very general and simple problems, they are useful also as readings for students who need a general acquaintance with some sample of experimental work in this field.

[1] 'Animal Intelligence: An Experimental Study of the Associative Processes in Animals' ('98), 'The Instinctive Reactions of Young Chicks' ('99), 'A Note on the Psychology of Fishes' ('99), and 'The Mental Life of the Monkeys' ('01). I have added a theoretical paper, 'The Evolution of the Human Intellect,' which appeared in the *Popular Science Monthly* in 1901, and which was a direct outgrowth of the experimental work. I am indebted to the management of the *Psychological Review*, and that of the *American Naturalist* and *Popular Science Monthly*, for permission to reprint the three shorter papers.

v

It has seemed best to leave the texts unaltered except for the correction of typographical errors, renumbering of tables and figures, and redrawing the latter. In a few places, where the original text has been found likely to be misunderstood, brief notes have been added. It is hard to resist the impulse to temper the style, especially of the 'Animal Intelligence,' with a certain sobriety and restraint. What one writes at the age of twenty-three is likely to irritate oneself a dozen years later, as it doubtless irritated others at the time. The charitable reader may allay his irritation by the thought that a degree of exuberance, even of arrogance, is proper to youth.

To the reports of experimental studies are added two new essays dealing with the general laws of human and animal learning.

JANUARY, 1911.

CONTENTS

viii *Contents*

ANIMAL INTELLIGENCE

ANIMAL INTELLIGENCE

CHAPTER I

THE STUDY OF CONSCIOUSNESS AND THE STUDY OF BEHAVIOR

THE statements about human nature made by psychologists are of two sorts, — statements about *consciousness*, about the inner life of thought and feeling, the 'self as conscious,' the 'stream of thought'; and statements about *behavior*, about the life of man that is left unexplained by physics, chemistry, anatomy and physiology, and is roughly compassed for common sense by the terms 'intellect' and 'character.'

Animal psychology shows the same double content. Some statements concern the conscious states of the animal, what he is to himself as an inner life; others concern his original and acquired ways of response, his behavior, what he is to an outside observer.

Of the psychological terms in common use, some refer only to conscious states, and some refer to behavior regardless of the consciousness accompanying it; but the majority are ambiguous, referring to the man or animal in question, at times in his aspect of inner life, at times in his aspect of reacting organism, and at times as an undefined total nature. Thus 'intensity,' 'duration' and 'quality' of sensations, 'transitive' and 'substantive' states and 'imagery' almost inevitably refer to states of conscious-

ness. 'Imitation,' 'invention' and 'practice' almost
inevitably refer to behavior observed from the outside.
'Perception,' 'attention,' 'memory,' 'abstraction,' 'reasoning' and 'will' are samples of the many terms which
illustrate both ways of studying human and animal
minds.   That an animal perceives an object, say, the sun,
may mean either that his mental stream includes an aware-
ness of that object distinguished from the rest of the visual
field; or that he reacts to that object as a unit.   'Attention' may mean a clearness, focalness, of the mental state;
or an exclusiveness and devotion of the total behavior.   It
may, that is, be illustrated by the sharpness of objects
illumined by a shaft of light, or by the behavior of a cat
toward the bird it stalks.   'Memory' may be consciousness of certain objects, events or facts; or may be the permanence of certain tendencies in either thought or action.
'To recognize' may be to feel a certain familiarity and
surety of being able to progress to certain judgments about
the thing recognized; or may be to respond to it in certain accustomed and appropriate ways.   'Abstraction' may
refer to ideas of qualities apart from any consciousness of
their concrete accompaniments, and to the power of having
such ideas; or to responses to qualities irrespective of their
concrete accompaniments, and to the power of making such
responses.   'Reasoning' may be said to be present when
certain sorts of consciousness, or when certain sorts of
behavior, are present.   An account of 'the will' is an
account of consciousness as related to action or an account
of the actions themselves.

Not only in psychological judgments and psychological
terms, but also in the work of individual psychologists,
this twofold content is seen.   Amongst writers in this
country, for example, Titchener has busied himself almost

exclusively with consciousness 'as such'; Stanley Hall, with behavior; and James, with both. In England Stout, Galton and Lloyd Morgan have represented the same division and union of interests.

On the whole, the psychological work of the last quarter of the nineteenth century emphasized the study of consciousness to the neglect of the total life of intellect and character. There was a tendency to an unwise, if not bigoted, attempt to make the science of human nature synonymous with the science of facts revealed by introspection. It was, for example, pretended that the only value of all the measurements of reaction-times was as a means to insight into the reaction-consciousness, — that the measurements of the amount of objective difference in the length, brightness or weight of two objects that men could judge with an assigned degree of correctness were of value only so far as they allowed one to infer something about the difference between two corresponding consciousnesses. It was affirmed that experimental methods were not to aid the experimenter to know what the subject did, but to aid the subject to know what he experienced.

The restriction of studies of human intellect and character to studies of conscious states was not without influence on scientific studies of animal psychology. For one thing, it probably delayed them. So long as introspection was lauded as the chief method of psychology, a psychologist would tend to expect too little from mere studies, from the outside, of creatures who could not report their inner experiences to him in the manner to which he was accustomed. In the literature of the time will be found many comments on the extreme difficulty of studying the psychology of animals and children. But difficulty exists only in the case of their *consciousness*. Their *behavior*, by its simpler nature and causation, is often far easier to study than that of adults. Again, much time was spent in argumentation about the criteria of consciousness, that is, about what certain common facts of behavior meant in reference to inner experience. The problems of inference about consciousness from behavior distracted attention from the problems of learning more about behavior itself. Finally, when psychologists began to observe and experiment upon animal behavior, they tended to overestimate the resulting insight into the stream of the animal's thought and to neglect the direct facts about what he did and how he did it.

Such observations and experiments are, however, themselves a means of restoring a proper division of attention between consciousness and behavior. A psychologist may think of himself as chiefly a stream of consciousness. He may even think of other men as chiefly conscious selves whose histories they report by word and deed. But it is only by an extreme bigotry that he can think of a dog or cat as chiefly a stream or chain or series of consciousness or consciousnesses. One of the lower animals is so obviously a bundle of original and acquired connections between situation and response that the student is led to attend to the whole series, — situation, response and connection or bond, — rather than to just the conscious state that may or may not be one of the features of the bond. It is so useful, in understanding the animal, to see what it does in different circumstances and what helps and what hinders its learning, that one is led to an intrinsic interest in varieties of behavior as well as in the kinds of consciousness of which they give evidence.

What each open-minded student of animal psychology at first hand comes thus to feel vaguely, I propose in this essay to try to make definite and clear. The studies reprinted in this volume produced in their author an increased respect for psychology as the science of behavior, a willingness to make psychology continuous with physiology, and a surety that to study consciousness for the sake of inferring what a man can or will do, is as proper as to study behavior for the sake of inferring what conscious states he can or will have. This essay will attempt to defend these positions and to show further that psychology may be, at least in part, as independent of introspection as physics is.

A psychologist who wishes to broaden the content of the science to include all that biology includes under the term 'behavior,' or all that common sense means by the words 'intellect' and 'character,' has to meet certain objections. The first is the indefiniteness of this content.

The indefiniteness is a fact, but is not in itself objectionable. It is true that by an animal's behavior one means the facts about the animal that are left over after geometry, physics, chemistry, anatomy and physiology have taken their toll, and that are not already well looked after by sociology, economics, history, esthetics and other sciences dealing with certain complex and specialized facts of behavior. It is true that the boundaries of psychology, from physiology on the one hand, and from sociology, economics and the like on the other, become dubious and changeable. But this is in general a sign of a healthy condition in a science. The pretense that there is an impassable cleft between physiology and psychology should arouse suspicion that one or the other science is studying words rather than realities.

The same holds against the objection that, if psychology is the science of behavior, it will be swallowed up by biology. When a body of facts treated subjectively, vaguely and without quantitative precision by one science or group of scientists comes to be treated more objectively, definitely and exactly by another, it is of course a gain, a symptom of the general advance of science. That geology may become a part of physics, or physiology a part of chemistry, is testimony ·to the advance of geology and physiology. Light is no less worthy of study by being found to be explainable by laws discovered in the study of electricity. Meteorology had to reach a relatively high development to provoke the wit to say that "All the science in meteorology is physics, the rest is wind."

These objections to be significant should frankly assert that between physical facts and mental facts, between bodies and minds, between any and all of the animal's movements and its states of consciousness, there is an impassable gap, a real discontinuity, found nowhere else in science; and that by making psychology responsible for territory on both sides of the gap, one makes psychology include two totally disparate group of facts, things and thoughts, requiring totally different methods of study. This is, of course, the traditional view of the scope of psychology, reiterated in the introductions to the standard books and often accepted in theory as axiomatic.

It has, however, already been noted that in practice psychologists do study facts in disregard of this supposed gap, that the same term refers to facts belonging some on one side of it and some on the other, and that, in animal psychology, it seems very unprofitable to try to keep on one side or the other. Moreover, the practice to which the study of animal and child psychology leads is, if I understand their writings, justified as a matter of theory by Dewey and Santayana. If then, as a matter of scientific fact, human and animal behavior, with or without consciousness, seems a suitable subject for a scientific student, we may study it without a too uneasy sense of philosophic heresy and guilt.

The writer must confess not only to the absence of any special reverence for the supposed axiom, but also to the presence of a conviction that it is false, the truth being that whatever feature of any animal, say John Smith, of *Homo sapiens*, is studied — its length, its color of hair, its body temperature, its toothache, its anxiety, or its thinking of 9×7 — the attitude and methods of the student may properly be substantially the same.

Of the six facts in the illustration just given, the last three would by the traditional view be all much alike for study, and all much unlike any of the first three. The same kind of science, physical science, would be potent for the first three and impotent for the last three (save to give facts about certain physical facts which ' paralleled' them). Conversely one kind of science, psychology, would by the traditional view deal with the last three, but have nothing to say about the first three.

But is there in actual fact any such radical dichotomy of these six facts as objects of science? Take any task of science with respect to them, for example, identification. A score of scientific men, including John Smith himself, are asked to identify John's stature at a given moment. Each observes it carefully, getting, let us say, as measures: 72.10 inches, 72.11, 72.05, 72.08, 72.09, 72.11, etc.

In the case of color of hair each observes as before, the reports being brown, light brown, brown, light brown, between light brown and brown, and so forth.

In the case of body temperature, again, each observes as before, there being the same variability in the reports; but John *may also observe in a second way*, not by observing

a thermometer with eyes, but by observing the temperature
of his body through other sense-organs so situated that
they lead to knowledge of only his own body's temperature.   It is important to note that for efficient knowledge
of his own body-temperature, John does not use the sense
approach peculiar to him, but that available for all observers.   He identifies and measures his 'feverishness' by
studying himself as he would study any other animal, by
thermometer and eye.

In the case of the toothache the students proceed as
before, except that they use John's gestures, facial expression, cries and verbal reports, as well as his mere
bodily structure and condition.   They not only observe the
cavities in his teeth, the signs of ulcer and the like, but they
also ask him, tapping a tooth, "Does it hurt?" "How
long has it hurt?" "Does it hurt very much?" and the
like.   John, if their equal in knowledge of dentistry, would
use the same methods, testing himself, asking himself
questions and using the replies made by himself to himself
in inner speech.   But, as with temperature, he would get
data, for his identification of the toothache, from a source
unavailable for the others, the sense-organs in his teeth.

It is worth while to consider how they and he would proceed to an exact identification or measure of the intensity
of his toothache such as was made of his stature or body-
temperature.   First, they would need a scale of toothaches
of varying intensities.   Next, they would need means of
comparing the intensity of his toothache with those of
this scale to see which it was most like.   Given this scale
and means of comparison, they would turn John's attention
from the original toothache to one of given intensity, and
compare the two, both by his facial expression, gestures and
the like, and by the verbal reports made.   John would

do likewise, reporting to himself instead of to them. The similarity of the procedure to that in studying a so-called physical fact is still clearer if we suppose a primitive condition of the scales of length and temperature. Suppose for example that for the length of a man we had only 'short' or 'tall as a deer,' 'medium' or 'tall as a moose,' and 'tall' or ' tall as a horse '; and for the intensity of the toothache of a man 'little' or 'intense as a pin-prick,' 'medium' or 'intense as a knife-cut,' and 'great' or 'intense as a spear-thrust.' Then obviously the only difference between the identification of the length of a man's body and the identification of the intensity of his toothache would be that the latter was made by all on the basis of behavior as well as anatomy, and made by the individual having it on the basis of data from an additional sense-organ.

In actual present practice, if observers were asked to identify the intensity of John's toothache on a scale running from zero intensity up, the variability of the reports would be very great in comparison with those of stature or body-temperature. Supposing the most intense toothache to be called K, we might well have reports of from say .300 K to .450 K, some observers identifying the fact with a condition one and a half times as intense as that chosen by others. But such a variability might also occur in primitive men's judgments of length or temperature.

It is important to note that the accuracy of John's own identification of it depends in any case on his knowledge of the scale and his power of comparing his toothache therewith. Well-trained outside observers might identify the intensity of John's toothache more accurately than he could.

In the case of John's anxiety, the most striking fact is the low degree of accuracy in identification. The quality of

the anxiety and its intensity would both be so crudely
measured by present means that even if the observers
were from the score of most competent psychologists, their
reports would probably be not much better than, say, the
descriptions now found in masterpieces of fiction and drama.
Science could not tell at all closely how much John's anxiety
at this particular time resembled either his anxiety on
some other occasion or anything else. This inferiority
is due in part to the fact that the manifestations of anxiety
in behavior, including verbal reports, are so complicated
by facts other than the anxiety itself, by, for example,
the animal's health, temperament, concomitant ideas
and emotions, knowledge of language, clearness in expression and the like. It is due in part to the very low status
of our classification of kinds of anxieties and of our units
and scales for measuring the amount of each kind. Hence
the variation amongst observers would be even greater
than in the case of the toothache, and the confidence of
all in their judgments would be less, and far, far less than
their confidence in their judgment of John's stature. The
best possible present knowledge of John's anxiety, though
scientific in comparison with ordinary opinion about it,
would seem grossly unscientific in comparison with knowledge of his stature or weight. Knowledge of the anxiety
would improve with better knowledge of its manifestations,
including verbal reports by John, and with better means of
classification and measurement.

John's knowledge of his own anxiety would be in part the
same as that of the other observers. He too would judge
his condition by its external manifestations, would name
its sort and rate its amount on the basis of his own behavior,
as he saw his own face, heard his own groans, and read the
notes he wrote describing his condition. But he would

also, as with the toothache, have data from internal sense-
organs and perhaps from centrally initiated neural actions.
In so far as he could report these data to himself for use
in scientific thought more efficiently than he could report
them to the other observers, he would have, as with the
toothache, an advantage comparable to the advantage
of a criminologist who happened also to be or to have been
a thief, or of a literary critic who happened to have written
what he judged. It is important to note that only in so
far as he who has 'immediate experience' of or participates
in or is 'directly conscious' of the anxiety, reports it to
himself as thinker or scientific student, in common with
the other nineteen, that this advantage accrues. To
really *be* or *have* the anxiety is not to correctly *know* it.
An insane man must become sane in order to know his
insane condition. Bigotry, stupidity and false reasoning
can be understood only by one who never was them or has
ceased to be them.

In our last illustration, John's thinking of '9 × 7 equals
63,' the effect on John's behavior may be so complicated
by other conditions in John, and is so subject to the particular conditions which we name John's 'will,' that the
observers would often be at loss except for John's verbal
report. Not that the observer is restricted to that. If
John does the example × $\overline{69}$ in the usual way, it is a very
safe inference that he thought 9 × 7 equals 63, regardless
of the absence of a verbal report from him. But often there
is little else to go by. To John himself, on the contrary,
it is easier to be sure that he is thinking of 9 × 7 equals
63, than that he has a particular sort and strength of toothache. Consequently if we suppose John to be thinking
of that fact while under observation, and the twenty ob-

servers to be required to identify the fact he is thinking of, it is sure that there might be an enormous variability in their guesses as to what the fact was and that his testimony might be worth far more than that of all the other nineteen without his testimony. His observation is influenced by the action of the neurones in his central nervous system as theirs is not, and, in the case of the thought '9 × 7 equals 63,' the action of these neurones is of special importance.

Our examination of the way science treats these six facts shows no impassable cleft between knowledge of a man's body and knowledge of his mind. Scientific statements about the toothache, anxiety and numerical judgment are in general more variable than statements about length, hair-color and body-temperature, but there is here no difference save of degree. Some physical facts, such as hair-color, eye-color or health, are, in fact, judged more variably than some mental facts, such as rate of adding, accuracy of perception of a certain sort and the like. So far as the lack of agreement amongst impartial observers goes, there is continuity from the identification of a length to that of an ideal.

Scientific judgments about the facts of John's mind also depend, in general, more upon his verbal reports than do judgments about his body. But here also the difference is only of degree. The physician studying wounds, ulcers, tumors, infections and other facts of a man's body may depend more upon his verbal reports than does the moralist who is studying the man's character. Verbal reports too are themselves a gradual and continuous extension of coarser forms of behavior. They signify consciousness no more truly than do signs, gestures, facial expression and the general bodily motions of pursuit, retreat, avoidance or seizure.

Nor is it true that physical facts are known to many observers and mental facts to but one, who *is* or *has* or *directly experiences* them. If it were true, sociology, economics, history, anthropology and the like would either be physical sciences or represent no knowledge at all. The kind of knowledge of which these sciences and the common judgments of our fellow men are made up is knowledge possessed by many observers in common, the individual of whom the facts is known, knowing the fact in part in just the same way that the others know it.

The real difference between a man's scientific judgments about himself and the judgment of others about him is that he has *added sources of knowledge.* Much of what goes on in him influences him in ways other than those in which it influences other men. But this difference is not coterminous with that between judgments about his 'mind' and about his 'body.' As was pointed out in the case of body-temperature, a man knows certain facts about his own body in such additional ways.

Furthermore, there is no more truth in the statement that a man's pain or anxiety or opinions are matters of direct consciousness, pure experience, than in the statement that his length, weight and temperature are, or that the sun, moon and stars are. If by the pain we must mean the pain as felt by some one, then by the sun we can mean only the sun as seen by some one. Pain and sun are equally subjects for a science of 'consciousness as such.' But if by the sun is meant the sun of common sense, physics and astronomy, the sun as known by any one, then by the pain we can mean the pain of medicine, economics and sociology, the pain as known by any one, and by the sufferer long after he *was* or *had* it.

All facts emerge from the matrix of pure experience;

but they become facts for science only after they have emerged therefrom. A man's anxiety may be the anxiety as directly felt by the man, or as thought of by him, or as thought of by the general consensus of scientific observers. But so also may be his body-temperature or weight or the composition of the blood in his veins. There can be no valid reason other than a pragmatic one for studying a man's anxiety solely as *felt* by him while studying his body-temperature as *thought of* by him and others. And the practical reasons are all in favor of studying all facts as they exist for any impartial observer. A man's mind as it is to thinking men is all that thinking men can deal with and all that they have any interest in dealing with.

Finally, the subject-matter of psychology is not sharply marked off from the subject-matter of physiology by being absolutely non-spatial. On the contrary, the toothache, anxiety and judgment are referred unequivocally, by every sane man who thinks of them, to the space occupied by the body of the individual in question. That is the surest fact about them. It is true that we do not measure the length, height, thickness and weight of an animal's pain or anxiety, but neither do we those of his pulse, temperature, health, digestion, metabolism, patellar reflex or heliotropism.

Two noteworthy advantages are secured by the study of behavior. First, the evidence about intellect and character offered by action and the influence of intellect and character upon action are given due attention. Second, the connections of conscious states are studied as well as their composition.

The mind or soul of the older psychology was the cause not only of consciousness, but also of modifiability in thought and action. It was the substance or force in man whereby he was sensitive to certain events, was able to make certain movements, and not only had ideas but connected them one with another and with various impressions and acts. It was supposed to account for actual bodily action as well as for the action-consciousness. It explained the connections between ideas as well as their internal composition. If a modern psychologist defines mind as the sum total of consciousness, and lives up to that definition, he omits the larger portion of the task of his predecessors. To define our subject-matter as the nature and behavior of men, beginning where anatomy and physiology leave off, is, on the contrary, to deliberately assume responsibility for the entire heritage. Behavior includes consciousness *and* action, states of mind *and* their connections.

Even students devoted to 'consciousness as such' must admit that the movements of an animal and their connections with other features of his life deserve study, by even their kind of psychologist. For the fundamental means of knowing that an animal has a certain conscious state are knowledge that it makes certain movements and knowledge of what conscious states are connected with those movements. Knowledge of the action-system of an animal and its connections is a prerequisite to knowledge of its stream of consciousness.

There are better reasons for including the action-system of an animal in the psychologist's subject-matter. An animal's conscious stream is of no account to the rest of the world except in so far as it prophesies or modifies his action.[1] There can be no moral warrant for studying man's nature unless the study will enable us to control his acts. If a psychologist is to study man's consciousness without relation to movement, he might as well fabricate

[1] Unless one assumes telepathic influences.

imaginary consciousnesses to describe and analyze. The
lovers of consciousness for its own sake often do this un-
wittingly, but would scarcely take pride therein!

The truth of the matter is, of course, that an animal's
mind is, by any definition, something intimately associated
with his connection-system or means of binding various
physical activities to various physical impressions. The
whole series — external situations and motor responses as
well as their bonds — must be studied to some extent in
order to understand whatever we define as mind. The
student of behavior, by frankly accepting the task of supply-
ing any needed information not furnished by physiology,
and of studying the animal in action as well as in thought,
is surer of getting an adequate knowledge of whatever
features of an animal's life may be finally awarded the title
of mind.

The second advantage in studying total behavior rather
than consciousness as such is that thereby the connections
of mental facts one with another and with non-mental facts
receive due attention.

The original tendencies to connect certain thoughts,
feelings and acts with certain situations — tendencies
which we call reflexes, instincts and capacities — are not
themselves states of consciousness; nor are the acquired
connections which we call habits, associations of ideas,
tendencies to attend, select and the like. No state of
consciousness bears within itself an account of when and
how it will appear, or of what bodily act will be its sequel.
What any given person will think in any given situation is
unpredictable by mere descriptions and analyses of his
previous thoughts each by itself. To understand the *when,
how* and *why* of states of consciousness one must study
other facts than states of consciousness. These non-

conscious relations or connections, knowledge of which informs us of the result to come from the action of a given situation on a given animal, may be expected to be fully half of the subject-matter of mental science.

As was noted in the early pages of this chapter, the psychologist commonly does adopt the attitude of treating mind as a system of connections long enough to give some account of the facts of instinct, habit, memory, and the like. But the dogma that psychology deals exclusively with the inner stream of mind-stuff has made these accounts needlessly scanty and vague.

One may appreciate fully the importance of finding out whether the attention-consciousness is clearness or is something else, and whether it exists in two or three discrete degrees or in a continuous series of gradations, and still insist upon the equal importance of finding out to what facts and for what reasons human beings do attend. There would appear, for example, to be an unfortunate limitation to the study of human nature by the examination of its consciousnesses, when two eminent psychologists, writing elaborate accounts of attention from that point of view, tell us almost nothing whereby we can predict what any given animal will attend to in any given situation, or can cause in any given animal a state of attention to any given fact.

One may enjoy the effort to define the kind of mind-stuff in which one thinks of classes of facts, relations between facts and judgments about facts, and still protest that a proper balance in the study of intellect demands equal or greater attention to the problems of why any given animal thinks of any given fact, class or relation in any given situation and why he makes this or that judgment about it.

In the case of the so-called action-consciousness the

neglect of the connections becomes preposterous. The adventitious scraps of consciousness called 'willing' which may intervene between a situation productive of a given act and the act itself are hopelessly uninstructive in comparison with the bonds of instinct and habit which cause the situation to produce the act. In conduct, at least, that kind of psychology which Santayana calls 'the perception of character' seems an inevitable part of a well-balanced science of human nature. I quote from his fine description of the contrast between the external observation of a mind's connections and the introspective recapitulation of its conscious content, though it is perhaps too pronounced and too severe.

"*Perception of Character.* — There is, however, a wholly different and far more positive method of reading the mind, or what in a metaphorical sense is called by that name. This method is to read character. Any object with which we are familiar teaches us to divine its habits; slight indications, which we should be at a loss to enumerate separately, betray what changes are going on and what promptings are simmering in the organism. . . . The gift of reading character . . . is directed not upon consciousness but upon past or eventual action. Habits and passions, however, have metaphorical psychic names, names indicating dispositions rather than particular acts (a disposition being mythically represented as a sort of wakeful and haunting genius waiting to whisper suggestions in a man's ear). We may accordingly delude ourselves into imagining that a pose or a manner which really indicates habit indicates feeling instead.

"*Conduct Divined, Consciousness Ignored.* . . . As the weather prophet reads the heavens, so the man of experience reads other men. Nothing concerns him less than their consciousness; he can allow that to run itself off when he is sure of their temper and habits. A great master of affairs is usually unsympathetic. His observation is not in the least dramatic or dreamful, he does not yield himself to animal contagion or reënact other people's inward experience. He is too busy for that, and too intent on his own purposes. His observation, on the contrary, is straight calculation and inference, and it sometimes reaches truths about people's character and destiny which they themselves are very far from divining. Such apprehension is masterful and odious to weaklings, who think they know themselves because they indulge in copious soliloquy (which is the discourse of brutes and madmen), but who really know nothing of their own capacity, situation, or fate." [1]

Mr. Santayana elsewhere hints that both psychology and history will become studies of human behavior considered from without, — a part, that is, of what he calls physics, — if they are to amount to much.

Such a prediction may come true. But for the present there is no need to decide which is better — to study an animal's self as conscious, its stream of direct experience, or to study the intellectual and moral nature that causes its behavior in thought and action and is known to many observers. Since worthy men have studied both, both are probably worthy of study. All that I wish to claim is the right of a man of science to study an animal's intellectual and moral behavior, following wherever the facts lead — to "the sum total of human experience considered as dependent upon the experiencing person," to the self as conscious, or to a connection-system known to many observers and born and bred in the animal's body.

[1] Reason in Common Sense, p. 154 ff.

CHAPTER II

ANIMAL INTELLIGENCE; AN EXPERIMENTAL STUDY OF THE ASSOCIATIVE PROCESSES IN ANIMALS [1]

THIS monograph is an attempt at an explanation of the nature of the process of association in the animal mind. Inasmuch as there have been no extended researches of a character similar to the present one either in subject-matter or experimental method, it is necessary to explain briefly its standpoint.

Our knowledge of the mental life of animals equals in the main our knowledge of their sense-powers, of their instincts or reactions performed without experience, and of their reactions which are built up by experience. Confining our attention to the latter, we find it the opinion of the better observers and analysts that these reactions can all be explained by the ordinary associative processes without aid from abstract, conceptual, inferential thinking. These associative processes then, as present in animals' minds and as displayed in their acts, are my subject-matter. Any one familiar in even a general way with the literature of comparative psychology will recall that this part of the field has received faulty and unsuccessful treatment. The careful, minute and solid knowledge of the sense-organs of animals finds no counterpart in the realm of associations and habits. We do not know how delicate or how complex or how permanent are the possible associations of any given group of animals. And although one would be rash who said that our present equipment of facts about instincts

[1] This chapter originally appeared as Monograph Supplement No. 8 of the Psychological Review.

was sufficient or that our theories about it were surely sound, yet our notion of what occurs when a chick grabs a worm are luminous and infallible compared to our notion of what happens when a kitten runs into the house at the familiar call. The reason that they have satisfied us as well as they have is just that they are so vague. We say that the kitten associates the sound 'kitty kitty' with the experience of nice milk to drink, which does very well for a common-sense answer. It also suffices as a rebuke to those who would have the kitten ratiocinate about the matter, but it fails to tell what real mental content is present. Does the kitten feel *"sound of call, memory-image of milk in a saucer in the kitchen, thought of running into the house, a feeling, finally, of 'I will run in'"*? Does he perhaps feel only the sound of the bell and an impulse to run in, similar in quality to the impulses which make a tennis player run to and fro when playing? The word 'association' may cover a multitude of essentially different processes, and when a writer attributes anything that an animal may do to association, his statement has only the negative value of eliminating reasoning on the one hand and instinct on the other. His position is like that of a zoölogist who should to-day class an animal among the 'worms.' To give to the word a positive value and several definite possibilities of meaning is one aim of this investigation.

The importance to comparative psychology in general of a more scientific account of the association-process in animals is evident. Apart from the desirability of knowing all the facts we can, of whatever sort, there is the especial consideration that these associations and consequent habits have an immediate import for biological science. In the higher animals the bodily life and preservative acts are largely directed by these associations. They, and not instinct, make the animal use the best feeding grounds, sleep in the same lair, avoid new dangers and profit by new changes in nature. Their higher development in mammals is a chief factor in the supremacy of that group. This, however, is a minor consideration. The main purpose of the study of the animal mind is to learn the development of mental life down through the phylum, to trace in particular the origin of human faculty. In relation to this chief purpose of comparative psychology the associative processes assume a rôle predominant over that of sense-powers or instinct, for in a study of the associative processes lies the solution of the problem. Sense-powers and instincts have changed by addition and supersedence, but the cognitive side of consciousness has changed not only in quantity but also in quality. Somehow out of these associative processes have arisen human consciousnesses with their sciences and arts and religions. The association of ideas proper, imagination, memory, abstraction, generalization, judgment, inference, have here their source. And in the metamorphosis the instincts, impulses, emotions and sense-impressions have been transformed out of their old natures. For the origin and development of human faculty we must look to these processes of association in lower animals. Not only then does this department need treatment more, but promises to repay the worker better.

Although no work done in this field is enough like the present investigation to require an account of its results, the *method* hitherto in use invites comparison by its contrast and, as I believe, by its faults. In the first place, most of the books do not give us a psychology, but rather a *eulogy*, of animals. They have all been about animal *intelligence*, never about animal *stupidity*. Though a writer derides the notion that animals have reason, he hastens to add that they have marvelous capacity of forming associations, and is likely to refer to the fact that human beings only rarely reason anything out, that their trains of ideas are ruled mostly by association, as if, in this latter, animals were on a par with them. The history of books on animals' minds thus furnishes an illustration of the well-nigh universal tendency in human nature to find the marvelous wherever it can. We wonder that the stars are so big and so far apart, that the microbes are so small and so thick together, and for much the same reason wonder at the things animals do. They used to be wonderful because of the mysterious, God-given faculty of instinct, which could almost remove mountains. More lately they have been wondered at because of their marvelous mental powers in profiting by experience. Now imagine an astronomer tremendously eager to prove the stars as big as possible, or a bacteriologist whose great scientific desire is to demonstrate the microbes to be very, very little! Yet there has been a similar eagerness on the part of many recent writers on animal psychology to praise the abilities of animals. It cannot help leading to partiality in deductions from facts and more especially in the choice of facts for investigation. How can scientists who write like lawyers, defending animals against the charge of having no power of rationality, be at the same time impartial judges on the bench? Unfortunately the real work in this field has been done in this spirit. The level-headed thinkers who might have won valuable results have contented themselves with arguing against the theories of the eulogists. They have not made investigations of their own.

In the second place, the facts have generally been derived from anecdotes. Now quite apart from such pedantry as insists that a man's word about a scientific fact is worthless

unless he is a trained scientist, there are really in this field
special objections to the acceptance of the testimony about
animals' intelligent acts which one gets from anecdotes.
Such testimony is by no means on a par with testimony
about the size of a fish or the migration of birds, etc.   For
here one has to deal not merely with ignorant or inaccurate
testimony, but also with prejudiced testimony.   Human
folk are as a matter of fact eager to find intelligence in
animals.   They like to.   And when the animal observed is
a pet belonging to them or their friends, or when the story
is one that has been told as a story to entertain, further
complications are introduced.   Nor is this all.   Besides
commonly misstating what facts they report, they report
only such facts as show the animal at his best.   Dogs get
lost hundreds of times and no one ever notices it or sends an
account of it to a scientific magazine.   But let one find his
way from Brooklyn to Yonkers and the fact immediately
becomes a circulating anecdote.   Thousands of cats on
thousands of occasions sit helplessly yowling, and no one
takes thought of it or writes to his friend, the professor;
but let one cat claw at the knob of a door supposedly as a
signal to be let out, and straightway this cat becomes the
representative of the cat-mind in all the books.   The unconscious distortion of the facts is almost harmless compared to the unconscious neglect of an animal's mental life
until it verges on the unusual and marvelous.   It is as if
some denizen of a planet where communication was by
thought-transference, who was surveying humankind and
reporting their psychology, should be oblivious to all our
intercommunication save such as the psychical-research
society has noted.   If he should further misinterpret the
cases of mere coincidence of thoughts as facts comparable
to telepathic communication, he would not be more wrong

than some of the animal psychologists. In short, the anecdotes give really the *abnormal* or *supernormal* psychology of animals.

Further, it must be confessed that these vices have been only ameliorated, not obliterated, when the observation is first-hand, is made by the psychologist himself. For as men of the utmost scientific skill have failed to prove good observers in the field of spiritualistic phenomena,[1] so biologists and psychologists before the pet terrier or hunted fox often become like Samson shorn. They, too, have looked for the intelligent and unusual and neglected the stupid and normal.

Finally, in all cases, whether of direct observation or report by good observers or bad, there have been three other defects. Only a single case is studied, and so the results are not necessarily true of the type; the observation is not repeated, nor are the conditions perfectly regulated; the previous history of the animal in question is not known. Such observations may tell us, if the observer is perfectly reliable, that a certain thing takes place; but they cannot assure us that it will take place universally among the animals of that species, or universally with the same animal. Nor can the influence of previous experience be estimated. All this refers to means of getting knowledge about what animals *do*. The next question is, "What do they *feel?*" Previous work has not furnished an answer or the material for an answer to this more important question. Nothing but carefully designed, crucial experiments can. In aban-

---

[1] I do not mean that scientists have been too credulous with regard to spiritualism, but am referring to the cases where ten or twenty scientists have been sent to observe some trick-performance by a spiritualistic 'medium,' and have all been absolutely confident that they understood the secret of its performance, *each of them giving a totally different explanation*.

doning the old method one ought to seek above all to replace it by one which will not only tell more accurately *what they do*, and give the much-needed information *how they do it*, but also inform us *what they feel* while they act.

To remedy these defects, experiment must be substituted for observation and the collection of anecdotes. Thus you immediately get rid of several of them. You can repeat the conditions at will, so as to see whether or not the animal's behavior is due to mere coincidence. A number of animals can be subjected to the same test, so as to attain typical results. The animal may be put in situations where its conduct is especially instructive. After considerable preliminary observation of animals' behavior under various conditions, I chose for my general method one which, simple as it is, possesses several other marked advantages besides those which accompany experiment of any sort. It was merely to put animals when hungry in inclosures from which they could escape by some simple act, such as pulling at a loop of cord, pressing a lever, or stepping on a platform. (A detailed description of these boxes and pens will be given later.) The animal was put in the inclosure, food was left outside in sight, and his actions observed. Besides recording his general behavior, special notice was taken of how he succeeded in doing the necessary act (in case he did succeed), and a record was kept of the time that he was in the box before performing the successful pull, or clawing, or bite. This was repeated until the animal had formed a perfect association between the sense-impression of the interior of that box and the impulse leading to the successful movement. When the association was thus perfect, the time taken to escape was, of course, practically constant and very short.

If, on the other hand, after a certain time the animal did not succeed, he was taken out, but *not fed*. If, after a suffi-

cient number of trials, he failed to get out, the case was recorded as one of complete failure. Enough different sorts
of methods of escape were tried to make it fairly sure that
association in general, not association of a particular sort of
impulse, was being studied. Enough animals were taken
with each box or pen to make it sure that the results were
not due to individual peculiarities. None of the animals
used had any previous acquaintance with any of the
mechanical contrivances by which the doors were opened.
So far as possible the animals were kept in a uniform state
of hunger, which was practically utter hunger.[1] That is,
no cat or dog was experimented on, when the experiment involved any important question of fact or theory,

[1] The phrase 'practically utter hunger' has given rise to misunderstand-
ings. I have been accused of experimenting with starving or half-starved
animals, with animals brought to a state of fear and panic by hunger, and
the like !

The desideratum is, of course, to have the motive as nearly as possible of
equal strength in each experiment with any one animal with any one act.
That is, the animal should be as hungry at the tenth or twentieth trial as at
the first. To attain this, the animal was given after each 'success' only
a very small bit of food as a reward (say, for a young cat, one quarter of a
cubic centimeter of fish or meat) and tested not too many times on any one
day. 'Utter hunger' means that no diminution in his appetite was noted
and that at the close of the experiment for the day he would still eat a hearty
meal. After the experiments for the day were done, the cats received
abundant food to maintain health, growth and spirits, but commonly somewhat less than they would of their own accord have taken. No one of the
many visitors to the room mentioned anything extraordinary or distressful
in the animals' condition. There were no signs of fear or panic.

Possibly I was wrong in choosing the term 'utter hunger' to denote the
hunger of an animal in good, but not pampered, condition and without food
for fourteen hours. It is not sure, however, that the term 'utter hunger'
is inappropriate. The few reports made of experiments in going without
food seem to show that, in health, the feeling of hunger reaches its maximum
intensity very early. It is of course not at all the same thing as the complex
of discomforts produced by long-continued insufficiency of food. Hunger
is not at all a synonym for starvation.

unless I was sure that his motive was of the standard strength.   With chicks this is not practicable, on account of their delicacy.   But with them dislike of loneliness acts as a uniform motive to get back to the other chicks.   Cats (or rather kittens), dogs and chicks were the subjects of the experiments.   All were apparently in excellent health, save an occasional chick.

By this method of experimentation the animals are put in situations which call into activity their mental functions and permit them to be carefully observed.   One may, by following it, observe personally more intelligent acts than are included in any anecdotal collection.   And this actual vision of animals in the act of using their minds is far more fruitful than any amount of history of what animals have done without the history of how they did it.   But besides affording this opportunity for purposeful and systematic observation, our method is valuable because it frees the animal from any influence of the observer.   The animal's behavior is quite independent of any factors save its own hunger, the mechanism of the box it is in, the food outside, and such general matters as fatigue, indisposition, etc. Therefore the work done by one investigator may be re- peated and verified or modified by another.   No personal factor is present save in the observation and interpretation. Again, our method gives some very important results which are quite uninfluenced by *any* personal factor in any way.   The curves showing the progress of the formation of associations, which are obtained from the records of the times taken by the animal in successive trials, are facts which may be obtained by any observer who can tell time.   They are absolute, and whatever can be deduced from them is sure.   So also the question of whether an animal does or does not form a certain association requires for an answer no higher qualification in the observer than a pair of eyes. The literature of animal psychology shows so uniformly and often so sadly the influence of the personal equation that any method which can partially eliminate it deserves a trial.

Furthermore, although the associations formed are such as could not have been previously experienced or provided for by heredity, they are still not too remote from the animal's ordinary course of life. They mean simply the connection of a certain act with a certain situation and resultant pleasure, and this general type of association is found throughout the animal's life normally. The muscular movements required are all such as might often be required of the animal. And yet it will be noted that the acts required are nearly enough like the acts of the anecdotes to enable one to compare the results of experiment by this method with the work of the anecdote school. Finally, it may be noticed that the method lends itself readily to experiments on imitation.

We may now start in with the description of the apparatus and of the behavior of the animals.[1]

DESCRIPTION OF APPARATUS

The shape and general apparatus of the boxes which were used for the cats is shown by the accompanying drawing of box K. Unless special figures are given, it should be understood that each box is approximately 20 inches long, by 15 broad, by 12 high. Except where mention is made to the contrary, the door was pulled open by a weight attached to a

[1] The experiments now to be described were for the most part made in the Psychological Laboratory of Columbia University during the year '97–'98, but a few of them were made in connection with a general preliminary investigation of animal psychology undertaken at Harvard University in the previous year.

string which ran over a pulley and was fastened to the door, just as soon as the animal loosened the bolt or bar which held it. Especial care was taken not to have the widest openings between the bars at all near the lever, or wire loop, or what not, which governed the bolt on the door.

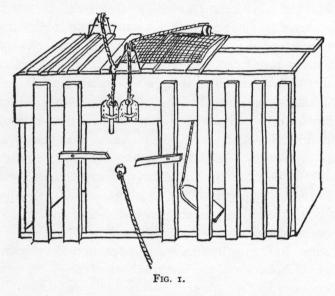

FIG. 1.

For the animal instinctively attacks the large openings first, and if the mechanism which governs the opening of the door is situated near one of them, the animal's task is rendered easier. You do not then get the association-process so free from the helping hand of instinct as you do if you make the box without reference to the position of the mechanism to be set up within it. These various mechanisms are so simple that a verbal description will suffice in most cases. The facts which the reader should note are the nature of the movement which the cat had to make, the nature of the object at which the movement was directed, and the position of the object in the box. In some special cases attention will also be called to the force required. In general, however, that was very slight (20 to 100 grams if applied directly). The various boxes will be designated by capital letters.

A. A string attached to the bolt which held the door ran up over a pulley on the front edge of the box, and was tied to a wire loop (2½ inches in diameter) hanging 6 inches above the floor in front center of box. Clawing or biting it, or rubbing against it even, if in a certain way, opened the door. We may call this box A '*O at front.*'

B. A string attached to the bolt ran up over a pulley on the front edge of the door, then across the box to another pulley screwed into the inside of the back of the box 1¼ inches below the top, and passing over it ended in a wire loop (3 inches in diameter) 6 inches above the floor in back center of box. Force applied to the loop or *to the string* as it ran across the top of the box between two bars would open the door. We may call B '*O at back.*'

B1. In B1 the string ran outside the box, coming down through a hole at the back, and was therefore inaccessible and invisible from within. Only by pulling the loop could the door be opened. B1 may be called '*O at back 2d.*'

C. A door of the usual position and size (as in Fig. 1) was kept closed by a wooden button 3½ inches long, ⅞ inch wide, ½ inch thick. This turned on a nail driven into the box ½ inch above the middle of the top edge of the door. The door would fall inward as soon as the button was turned from its vertical to a horizontal position. A pull of 125 grams would do this if applied sideways at the lowest point of the button 2¼ inches below its pivot. The cats usually clawed the button round by downward pressure on its top edge, which was 1¼ inches above the nail. Then, of course, more force was necessary. C may be called '*Button.*'

D. The door was in the extreme right of the front. A string fastened to the bolt which held it ran up over a pulley on the top edge and back to the top edge of the back side of the box (3 inches in from the right side) and was there firmly fastened. The top of the box was of wire screening and arched over the string ¾ inch above it along its entire length. A slight pull on the string anywhere opened the door. This box was 20 × 16, but a space 7 × 16 was partitioned off at the left by a wire screen. D may be called '*String*.'

D1 was the same box as B, but had the string fastened firmly at the back instead of running over a pulley and ending in a wire loop. We may call it '*String 2d*.'

E. A string ran from the bolt holding the door up over a pulley and down to the floor outside the box, where it was fastened 2 inches in front of the box and 1½ inches to the left of the door (looking from the inside). By poking a paw out between the bars and pulling this string inward the door would be opened. We may call E '*String outside*.'

In F the string was not fastened to the floor but ended in a loop 2½ inches in diameter which could be clawed down so as to open the door. Unless the pull was in just the right direction, the string was likely to catch on the pulley. This loop hung 3 inches above the floor, and 1¾ inches in front of the box. We may call F '*String outside unfastened*.'

G was a box 29 × 20½ × 22½, with a door 29 × 12 hinged on the left side of the box (looking from within), and kept closed by an ordinary thumb latch placed 15 inches from the floor. The remainder of the front of the box was closed in by wooden bars. The door was a wooden frame covered with screening. It was *not* arranged so as to open as soon as the latch was lifted, but required a force of 400 grams, even when applied to the best advantage. The bar of the thumb latch, moreover, would fall back into place again unless the door were pushed out at least a little. The top of this box was not of bars or screening, but solid. We may call G '*Thumb latch.*'

H was, except for the opening where the door was situated, a perfectly solid and dark box. In the front was cut an opening about 9 × 7 inches. A wooden frame covered with wire netting hung in front of this. It was fastened to the box only by a screw through the middle of the frame's top piece, and could therefore be pushed to either side so as to permit escape from the box if it were prevented from swinging back into place.

I was a box 12 × 14 × 23. The door was 8 inches wide, 4 high, and hinged at the left side. It was held closed by a wooden bar which moved easily on a pivot and which could be pushed up by another bar which projected 5 inches into the box. This second bar was pivoted so that downward pressure on it pushed the first bar up and let the door swing open. The second bar entered the box at a point 4 inches above the floor and $2\frac{1}{2}$ inches in from the right side of the box. In its normal position its inner end was $5\frac{1}{2}$ inches above the floor. A depression of 2 inches at that end was necessary to open the door. Of course, nearer the pivot a shorter depression would do. The front of the box was closed by bars, but the rest by solid boards. We may call I '*Lever.*'

J was the same as B except that the door was not opened by a weight as soon as the bolt was pulled up. On the contrary, the door was held closed by a small piece of board $(4 \times 3\frac{1}{2} \times \frac{3}{4}$ thick) placed against it outside. After pulling the loop at the back the cat had to knock down this support and push the door open. We may call J '*Double.*'

K was a box arranged so that three separate acts were required to open the door, which was held by two bolts at the top and two bars outside. One of the bolts was connected with a platform in the back center of the box so that depressing the platform raised the bolt. The other was raised by a string which ran up over a pulley in the front, across the box 1 inch above the bars, over a pulley near the corner of the box, and down to the floor, where it was fastened. Pulling on this string, either by clawing at it where it was running vertically from the last pulley to the floor, or by putting the paw out between the bars which covered the top of the box, and clawing the string downward, would raise the bolt. If both bolts were raised and *either* bar was pushed up or down far enough to be out of the way, the cat could escape. K, or '*Triple*,' as it may be called, is the box reproduced in Figure 1.

L was a box that also required three acts to open the door. It was a combination of A (O at front), D (string), I (lever). The lever or bar to be depressed was 2 inches to the right of the door, which was in the front center. The string to be clawed or bitten ran from front center to back center 1 inch below the top of the box.

Z was a box with back and sides entirely closed, with front and top closed by bars and screening, with a small opening in the left-hand corner. A box was held in front of this and drawn away when the cats happened to lick themselves. Thus escape and food followed always upon the impulse to lick themselves, and they soon would immediately start doing so as soon as pushed into the box. The same box was used with the impulse changed to that for scratching themselves. The size of this box was 15 × 10 × 16.

EXPERIMENTS WITH CATS

In these various boxes were put cats from among the following. I give approximately their ages while under experiment.

No. 1. 8–10 months.	No. 7. 3–5 months.
No. 2. 5–7 months.	No. 8. 6–6½ months.
No. 3. 5–11 months.	No. 10. 4–8 months.
No. 4. 5–8 months.	No. 11. 7–8 months.
No. 5. 5–7 months.	No. 12. 4–6 months.
No. 6. 3–5 months.	No. 13. 18–19 months.

The behavior of all but 11 and 13 was practically the same. When put into the box the cat would show evident signs of discomfort and of an impulse to escape from confinement. It tries to squeeze through any opening; it claws and bites at the bars or wire; it thrusts its paws out through any opening and claws at everything it reaches; it continues its efforts when it strikes anything loose and shaky; it may claw at things within the box. It does not pay very much attention to the food outside, but seems simply to strive instinctively to escape from confinement. The vigor with which it struggles is extraordinary. For eight or ten minutes it will claw and bite and squeeze incessantly. With 13, an old cat, and 11, an uncommonly sluggish cat, the behavior was different. They did not struggle vigorously or continually. On some occasions they did not even struggle at all. It was therefore necessary to let them out of some box a few times, feeding them each time. After they thus associate climbing out of the box with getting food, they will try to get out whenever put in. They do not, even then, struggle so vigorously or get so excited as the rest. In either case, whether the impulse to struggle be due to an instinctive reaction to confinement or to an association, it is likely to succeed in letting the cat out of the box. The cat that is clawing all over the box in her impulsive struggle will probably claw the string or loop or button so as to open the door. And gradually all the other non-successful impulses will be stamped out and the particular impulse leading to the successful act will be stamped in by the resulting pleasure, until, after many trials, the cat will, when put in the box, immediately claw the button or loop in a definite way.

The starting point for the formation of any association in these cases, then, is the set of instinctive activities which are aroused when a cat feels discomfort in the box either because of confinement or a desire for food. This discomfort, plus the sense-impression of a surrounding, confining wall, expresses itself, prior to any experience, in squeezings, clawings, bitings, etc. From among these movements one is selected by success. But this is the starting point only in the case of the first box experienced. After that the cat has associated with the feeling of confinement certain impulses which have led to success more than others and are thereby strengthened. A cat that has learned to escape from A by clawing has, when put into C or G, a greater tendency to claw at things than it instinctively had at the start, and a less tendency to squeeze through holes. A very pleasant form of this decrease in instinctive impulses was noticed in the gradual cessation of howling and mewing. However, the useless instinctive impulses die out slowly, and often play an important part even after the cat has had experience with six or eight boxes. And what is important in our previous statement, namely, that the activity of an animal when first put into a new box is not directed by any appreciation of *that* box's character, but by certain general impulses to act, is not affected by this modification. Most of this activity is determined by heredity; some of it, by previous experience.

My use of the words *instinctive* and *impulse* may cause some misunderstanding unless explained here. Let us, throughout this book, understand by instinct any reaction which an animal makes to a situation *without experience*. It thus includes unconscious as well as conscious acts. Any reaction, then, to totally new phenomena, when first experienced, will be called instinctive. Any impulse then felt will be called an instinctive impulse. Instincts include whatever the nervous system of an animal, as far as inherited, is capable of. My use of the word will, I hope, everywhere make clear what fact I mean. If the reader gets the fact meant in mind it does not in the least matter whether he would himself call such a fact instinct or not. Any one who objects to the word may substitute 'hocus-pocus' for it wherever it occurs. The definition here made will not be used to prove or disprove any theory, but simply as a signal for the reader to imagine a certain sort of fact.

The word *impulse* is used against the writer's will, but there is no better. Its meaning will probably become clear as the reader finds it in actual use, but to avoid misconception at any time I will state now that *impulse* means the consciousness accompanying a muscular innervation *apart from that feeling of the act which comes from seeing oneself move, from feeling one's body in a different position, etc.* It is the *direct feeling of the doing* as distinguished from the *idea of the act done* gained through eye, etc. For this reason I say 'impulse *and* act' instead of simply 'act.' Above all, it must be borne in mind that by impulse I never mean the *motive* to the act. In popular speech you may say that hunger is the impulse which makes the cat claw. That

will never be the use here. The word *motive* will always
denote that sort of consciousness. Any one who thinks
that the act ought not to be thus subdivided into impulse
and deed may feel free to use the word *act* for *impulse* or *impulse and act* throughout, if he will remember that the act
in this aspect of being felt as to be done or as doing is in
animals the important thing, is the thing which gets associated, while the act as done, as viewed from outside, is a
secondary affair. I prefer to have a separate word, *impulse*,
for the former, and keep the word *act* for the latter, which it
commonly means.

Starting, then, with its store of instinctive impulses,
the cat hits upon the successful movement, and gradually
associates it with the sense-impression of the interior of the
box until the connection is perfect, so that it performs the
act as soon as confronted with the sense-impression. The
formation of each association may be represented graphically by a time-curve. In these curves lengths of one millimeter along the abscissa represent successive experiences
in the box, and heights of one millimeter above it each
represent ten seconds of time. The curve is formed by
joining the tops of perpendiculars erected along the abscissa
1 mm. apart (the first perpendicular coinciding with the *y*
line), each perpendicular representing the time the cat was
in the box before escaping. Thus, in Fig. 2 on page 39 the
curve marked *12 in A* shows that, in 24 experiences or
trials in box A, cat 12 took the following times to perform
the act, 160 sec., 30 sec., 90 sec., 60, 15, 28, 20, 30, 22, 11, 15,
20, 12, 10, 14, 10, 8, 8, 5, 10, 8, 6, 6, 7. A short vertical line
below the abscissa denotes that an interval of approximately
24 hours elapsed before the next trial. Where the interval
was longer it is designated by a figure 2 for two days, 3 for
three days, etc. If the interval was shorter, the number of

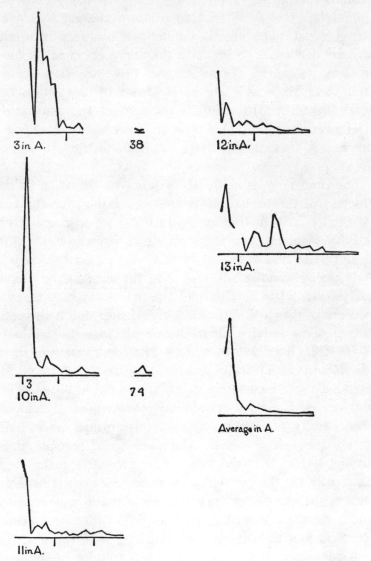

Fig. 2.

hours is specified by 1 hr., 2 hrs., etc. In many cases the
animal failed in some trial to perform the act in ten or
fifteen minutes and was then taken out by me. Such failures are denoted by a break in the curve either at its start
or along its course. In some cases there are short curves
after the main ones. These, as shown by the figures be-
neath, represent the animal's mastery of the association
after a very long interval of time, and may be called memory-
curves. A discussion of them will come in the last part of
the chapter.

The time-curve is obviously a fair representation of the
progress of the formation of the association, for the two
essential factors in the latter are the disappearance of all
activity save the particular sort which brings success with
it, and perfection of that particular sort of act so that it is
done precisely and at will. Of these the second is, on deeper
analysis, found to be a part of the first; any clawing at a
loop except the particular claw which depresses it is theoretically a useless activity. If we stick to the looser phraseology,
however, no harm will be done. The combination of these
two factors is inversely proportional to the time taken,
provided the animal surely wants to get out at once. This
was rendered almost certain by the degree of hunger.
Theoretically a perfect association is formed when both
factors are perfect, — when the animal, for example, does
nothing but claw at the loop, and claws at it in the most
useful way for the purpose. In some cases (*e.g.* 2 in K on
page 53) neither factor ever gets perfected in a great many
trials. In some cases the first factor does but the second
does not, and the cat goes at the thing not always in the
desirable way. In all cases there is a fraction of the time
which represents getting oneself together after being
dropped in the box, and realizing where one is. But for

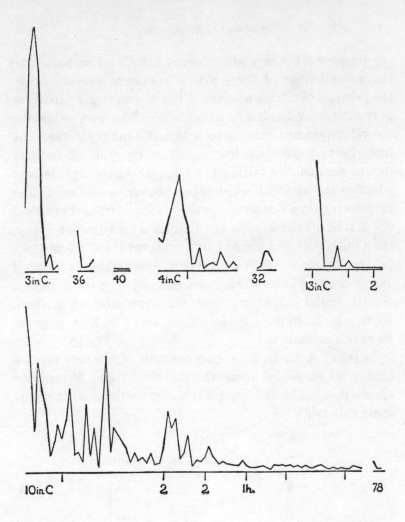

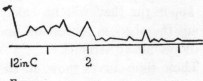

FIG. 3.

our purpose all these matters count little, and we may take
the general slope of the curve as representing very fairly
the progress of the association.   The slope of any particular
part of it may be due to accident.   Thus, very often the
second experience may have a higher time-point than the
first, because the first few successes may all be entirely
due to accidentally hitting the loop, or whatever it is, and
whether the accident will happen sooner in one trial than
another is then a matter of chance.   Considering the general
slope, it is, of course, apparent that a gradual descent — say,
from initial times of 300 sec. to a constant time of 6 or 8 sec.
in the course of 20 to 30 trials —represents a difficult
association; while an abrupt descent, say in 5 trials, from a
similar initial height, represents a very easy association.
Thus, 2 in Z, on page 57, is a hard, and 1 in I, on page 49,
an easy association.

In boxes A, C, D, E, I, 100 per cent of the cats given a
chance to do so, hit upon the movement and formed the
association.   The following table shows the results where
some cats failed: —

TABLE I

	No. Cats Tried	No. Cats Failed
F	5	4
G	8	5
H	9	2
J	5	2
K	5	2

The time-curves follow.   By referring to the description
of apparatus they will be easily understood.   Each mm.
along the abscissa represents one trial.   Each mm. above
it represents 10 seconds.

These time-curves show, in the first place, what associa-

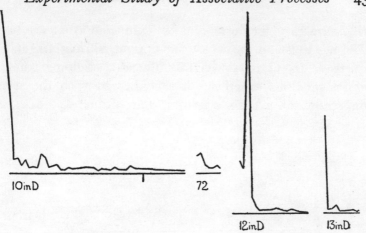

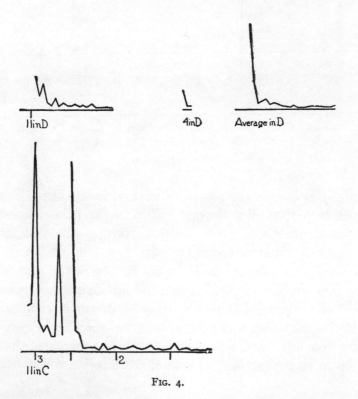

FIG. 4.

tions are easy for an animal to form, and what are hard. The act must be one which the animal will perform in the course of the activity which its inherited equipment incites or its previous experience has connected with the sense-impression of a box's interior. The oftener the act nat-

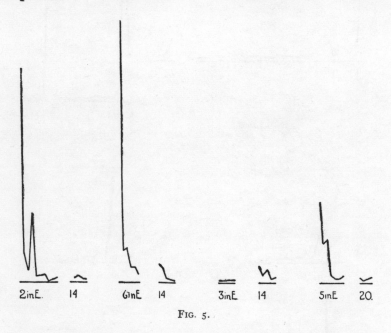

FIG. 5.

urally occurs in the course of such activity, the sooner it will be performed in the first trial or so, and this is one condition, sometimes, of the ease of forming the association. For if the first few successes are five minutes apart, the influence of one may nearly wear off before the next, while if they are forty seconds apart the influences may get summated. But this is not the only or the main condition of the celerity with which an association may be formed. It depends also on the amount of attention given to the act. An act of the sort likely to be well attended to will be learned

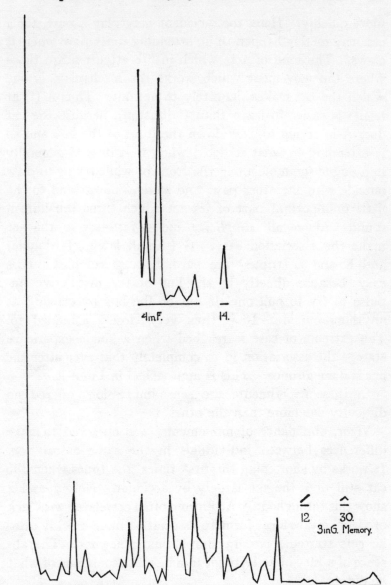

FIG. 6.

more quickly. Here, too, accident may play a part, for a cat may merely happen to be attending to its paw when it claws. The kind of acts which insure attention are those where the movement which works the mechanism is one which the cat makes definitely to get out. Thus A (O at front) is easier to learn than C (button), because the cat does A in trying to claw down the front of the box and so is attending to what it does; whereas it does C generally in a vague scramble along the front or while trying to claw outside with the other paw, and so does not attend to the little unimportant part of its act which turns the button round. Above all, *simplicity* and *definiteness* in the act make the association easy. G (thumb latch), J (double) and K and L (triples) are hard, because complex. E is easy, because directly in the line of the instinctive impulse to try to pull oneself out of the box by clawing at anything outside. It is thus very closely attended to. The extreme of ease is reached when a single experience stamps the association in so completely that ever after the act is done at once. This is approached in I and E.

In these experiments the sense-impressions offered no difficulty one more than the other.

Vigor, abundance of movements, was observed to make differences between individuals in the same association. It works by shortening the first times, the times when the cat still does the act largely by accident. Nos. 3 and 4 show this throughout. Attention, often correlated with lack of vigor, makes a cat form an association more quickly after he gets started. No. 13 shows this somewhat. The absence of a fury of activity let him be more conscious of what he did do.

The curves on pages 57 and 58, showing the history of cats 1, 5, 13 and 3, which were let out of the box Z when

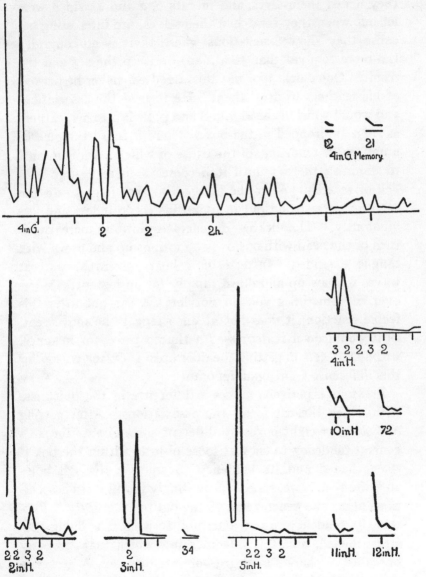

FIG. 7.

they licked themselves, and of cats 6, 2 and 4, which were let out when they scratched themselves, are interesting because they show associations where there is no congruity (no more to a cat than to a man) between the act and the result. One chick, too, was thus freed whenever he pecked at his feathers to dress them. He formed the association, and would whirl his head round and poke it into his feathers as soon as dropped in the box. There is in all these cases a noticeable tendency, of the cause of which I am ignorant, to diminish the act until it becomes a mere vestige of a lick or scratch. After the cat gets so that it performs the act soon after being put in, it begins to do it less and less vigorously. The licking degenerates into a mere quick turn of the head with one or two motions up and down with tongue extended. Instead of a hearty scratch, the cat waves its paw up and down rapidly for an instant. Moreover, if sometimes you do not let the cat out after this feeble reaction, it does not at once repeat the movement, as it would do if it depressed a thumb piece, for instance, without success in getting the door open. Of the reason for this difference I am again ignorant.

Previous experience makes a difference in the quickness with which the cat forms the associations. After getting out of six or eight boxes by different sorts of acts the cat's general tendency to claw at loose objects within the box is strengthened and its tendency to squeeze through holes and bite bars is weakened; accordingly it will learn associations along the general line of the old more quickly. Further, its tendency to pay attention to what it is doing gets strengthened, and this is something which may properly be called a change in degree of intelligence. A test was made of the influence of experience in this latter way by putting two groups of cats through I (lever), one group

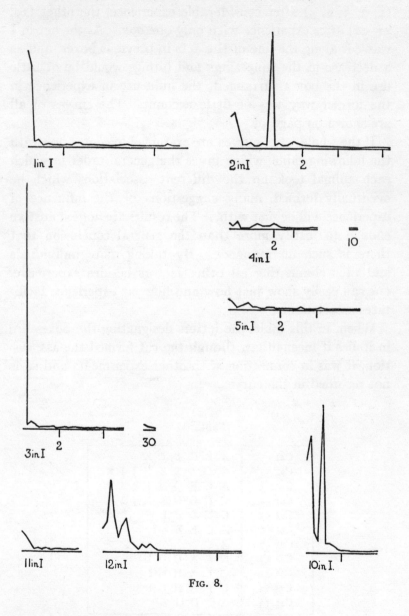

FIG. 8.

(1, 2, 3, 4, 5) after considerable experience, the other (10, 11, 12) after experience with only one box. As the act in I was not along the line of the acts in previous boxes, and as a decrease in the squeezings and bitings would be of little use in the box as arranged, the influence of experience in the former way was of little account. The curves of all are shown on page 49.

If the whole set of curves are examined in connection with the following table, which gives the general order in which each animal took up the different associations which he eventually formed, many suggestions of the influence of experience will be met with. The results are not exhaustive enough to justify more than the general conclusion that there is such an influence. By taking more individuals and thus eliminating all other factors besides experience, one can easily show just how and how far experience facilitates association.

When, in this table, the letters designating the boxes are in italics it means that, though the cat formed the association, it was in connection with other experiments and so is not recorded in the curves.

TABLE II

Cat 1	A B C D_1 D Z I
Cat 2	C D_1 D E Z H J I K
Cat 3	A C E G H J Z I K
Cat 4	C F G D Z H J I K
Cat 5	C E Z H I
Cat 6	A C E Z
Cat 7	A C
Cat 10	C I A H D L
Cat 11	C I A H D L
Cat 12	C I A H D L
Cat 13	A C D G Z

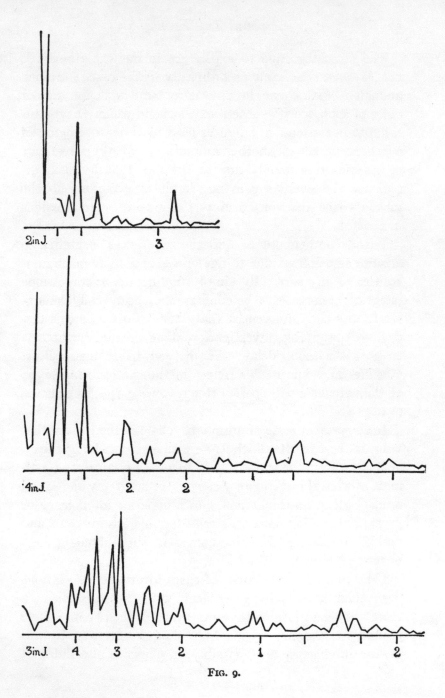

FIG. 9.

The advantage due to experience in our experiments is not, however, the same as ordinarily in the case of trained animals. With them the associations are with the acts or voice of man or with sense-impressions to which they naturally do not attend (*e.g.* figures on a blackboard, ringing of a bell, some act of another animal). Here the advantage of experience is mainly due to the fact that by such experience the animals gain the habit of attending to the master's face and voice and acts and to sense-impressions in general.

I made no attempt to find the differences in ability to acquire associations due to age or sex or fatigue or circumstances of any sort. By simply finding the average slope in the different cases to be compared, one can easily demonstrate any such differences that exist. So far as this discovery is profitable, investigation along this line ought now to go on without delay, the method being made clear. Of differences due to differences in the species, genus, etc., of the animals I will speak after reviewing the time-curves of dogs and chicks.

In the present state of animal psychology there is another value to these results which was especially aimed at by the investigator from the start. They furnish a quantitative estimate of what the average cat can do, so that if any one has an animal which he thinks has shown superior intelligence or perhaps reasoning power, he may test his observations and opinion by taking the time-curves of the animal in such boxes as I have described.

If his animal in a number of cases forms the associations very much more quickly, or deals with the situation in a more intelligent fashion than my cats did, then he may have ground for claiming in his individual a variation toward greater intelligence and, possibly, intelligence of a different

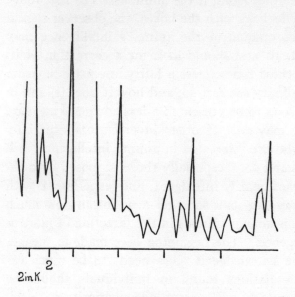

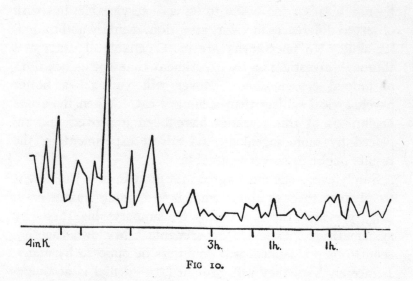

FIG 10.

order. On the other hand, if the animal fails to rise above the type in his dealings with the boxes, the observer should confess that his opinion of the animal's intelligence may have been at fault and should look for a correction of it.

We have in these time-curves a fairly adequate measure of what the ordinary cat can do, and how it does it, and in similar curves soon to be presented a less adequate measure of what a dog may do. If other investigators, especially all amateurs who are interested in animal intelligence, will take other cats and dogs, especially those supposed by owners to be extraordinarily intelligent, and experiment with them in this way, we shall soon get a notion of how much variation there is among animals in the direction of more or superior intelligence. The beginning here made is meager but solid. The knowledge it gives needs to be much extended. The variations found in individuals should be correlated, not merely with supposed superiority in intelligence, a factor too vague to be very serviceable, but with observed differences in vigor, attention, memory and muscular skill. No phenomena are more capable of exact and thorough investigation by experiment than the associations of animal consciousness. Never will you get a better psychological subject than a hungry cat. When the crude beginnings of this research have been improved and replaced by more ingenious and adroit experimenters, the results ought to be very valuable.

Surely every one must agree that no man now has a right to advance theories about what is in animals' minds or to deny previous theories unless he supports his thesis by systematic and extended experiments. My own theories, soon to be proclaimed, will doubtless be opposed by many. I sincerely hope they will, provided the denial is accompanied by actual experimental work. In fact, I shall be tempted

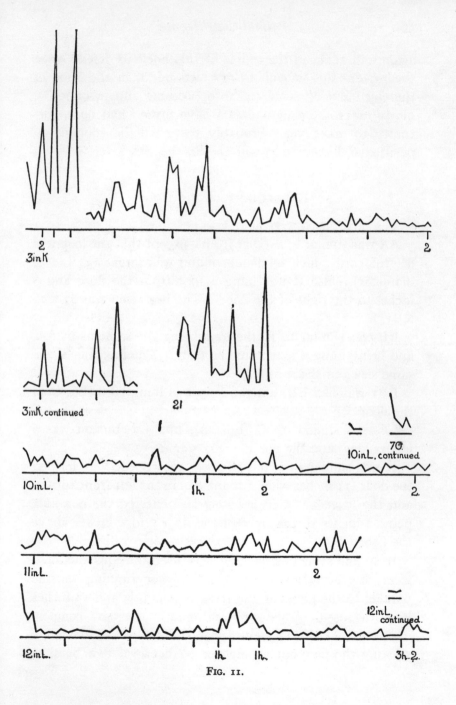

FIG. II.

again and again in the course of this book to defend some theory, dubious enough to my own mind, in the hope of thereby inducing some one to oppose me and in opposing me to make the experiments I have myself had no opportunity to make yet. Probably there will be enough opposition if I confine myself to the theories I feel sure of.

Experiments with Dogs

The boxes used were as follows:

AA was similar to A (O at front), except that the loop was of stiff cord $\frac{3}{8}$ inch in diameter and was larger ($3\frac{1}{2}$ inches diameter); also it was hung a foot from the floor and 8 inches to the right of the door. The box itself was 41 × 20 × 23.

BB was similar to B, the loop being the same as in AA, and being hung a foot from the floor. The box was of the same size and shape as AA.

BB1 was like BB, but the loop was hung 18 inches from the floor.

CC was similar to C (button), but the button was 6 inches long, and the box was $36\frac{1}{2}$ × 22 × 23.

II was similar to I, but the box was 30 × 20 × 25 inches; the door (11 inches wide, 6 high) was in the left front corner, and the lever was 6 inches long and entered the box at a point 2 inches to the right of the door and 4 inches above the floor.

In M the same box as in II was used, but instead of a lever projecting inside the box, a lever running outside parallel to the plane of the front of the box and 18 inches long was used. This lay close against the bars composing the front of the box, and could be pawed down by sticking the paw out an inch or so between two bars, at

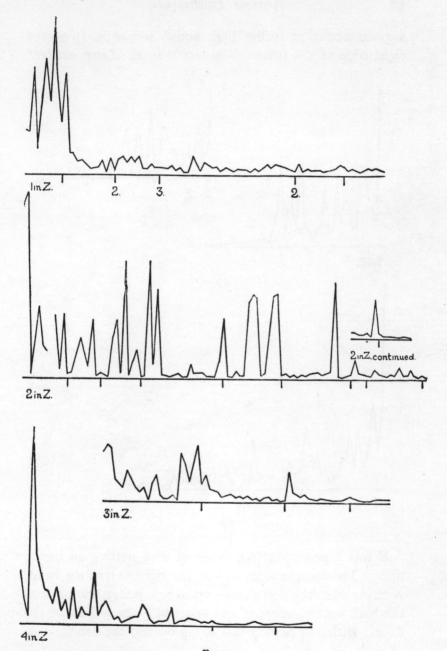

1 in Z.   2.   3.   2.

2 in Z.   2 in Z. continued.

3 in Z.

4 in Z

FIG. 12.

a point about 15 inches high and 6 inches in from the
right edge of the front. We may call M '*Lever outside.*'

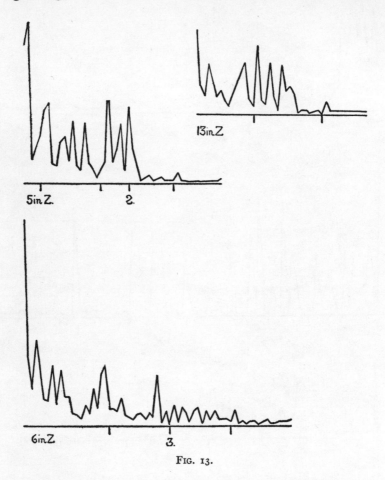

FIG. 13.

N was a pen 5 × 3 feet made of wire netting 46 inches
high. The door, 31 × 20, was in the right half of the front.
A string from the bolt passed up over a pulley and back to
the back center, where it was fastened 33 inches above the
floor. Biting or pawing this string opened the door.

O was like K, except that there was only one bar, that the string ran inside the box, so that it was easily accessible, and that the bolt raised in K by depression of the platform could be raised in O (and was by the dog experimented on) by sticking the muzzle out between two bars just above the bolt and by biting the string, at the same time jerking it upward. O was 30 × 20 × 25 in size.

The box G was used for both dogs and cats, without any variation save that for dogs the resistance of the door to pressure outwards was doubled.

In these boxes were put in the course of the experiments dog 1 (about 8 months old), and dogs 2 and 3, adults, all of small size.

A dog who, when hungry, is shut up in one of these boxes is not nearly so vigorous in his struggles to get out as is the young cat. And even after he has experienced the pleasure of eating on escape many times he does not try to get out so hard as a cat, young or old. He does try to a certain extent. He paws or bites the bars or screening, and tries to squeeze out in a tame sort of way. He gives up his attempts sooner than the cat, if they prove unsuccessful. Furthermore his attention is taken by the food, not the confinement. He wants to get *to* the food, not *out of* the box. So, unlike the cat, he confines his efforts to the front of the box. It was also a practical necessity that the dogs should be kept from howling in the evening, and for this reason I could not use as motive the utter hunger which the cats were made to suffer. In the morning, when the experiments were made, the dogs were surely hungry, and no experiment is recorded in which the dog was not in a state to be willing to make a great effort for a bit of meat, but the motive may not have been even and equal throughout, as it was with the cats.

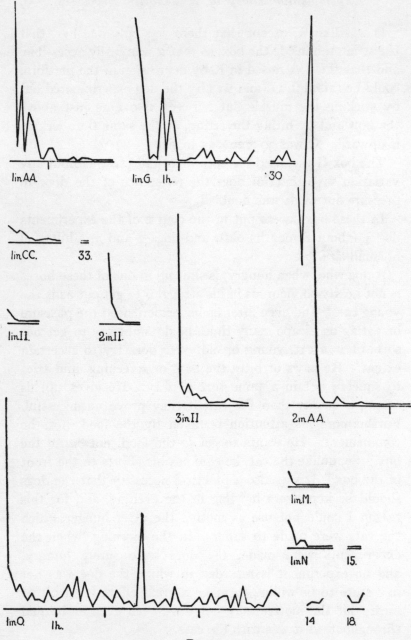

FIG. 14.

The curves on page 60 are to be interpreted in the same way as those for the cats, and are on the same scale. The order in which No. 1 took up the various associations was AA, BB, BB1, G, N, CC, II, O.

The percentage of dogs succeeding in the various boxes is given below, but is of no consequence, because so few were tried, and because the motive, hunger, was not perhaps strong enough, or equal in all cases.

In AA 3 out of 3.

In BB 0 out of 2 (that is, without previous experience of AA).

In CC 1 out of 2.

In II 3 out of 3.

In M 1 out of 2.

In N 1 out of 3.

In G 1 out of 3.

EXPERIMENTS WITH CHICKS

The apparatus was as follows:

P was simply a small pen arranged with two exits, one leading to the inclosure where were the other chicks and

FIG. 15.   FIG. 16.   FIG. 17.

food, one leading to another pen with no exit. The drawing (Fig. 15 on this page) explains itself. A chick was placed at A and left to find its way out. The walls were made of books stuck up on end.

Q was a similar pen arranged so that the real exit was harder to find. (See Fig. 16.)

R was still another pen similarly constructed, with four possible avenues to be taken. (See Fig. 17.)

S was a pen with walls 11 inches high. On the right side an inclined plane of wire screening led from the floor of the pen to the top of its front wall. Thence the chick could jump down to where its fellows and the food and drink were. S was 17×14 in size.

T was a pen of the same size as S, with a block of wood 3 inches by 3 and 2 inches high in the right back corner. From this an inclined plane led to the top of the front wall (on the right side of the box). But a partition was placed along the left edge of this plane, so that a chick could reach it only *via* the wooden block, not by a direct jump.

U was a pen 16×14×10 inches. Along the back toward the right corner were placed a series of steps $1\frac{1}{2}$ inches wide, the first 1, the second 2, and the third 3 inches high. In the corner was a platform 4×4, and 4 high, from which access to the top of the front wall of the pen could be gained by scrambling up inside a stovepipe 11 inches long, inclined upward at an angle of about 30°. From the edge of the wall the chick could, of course, jump down to food and society. The top of the pen was covered so that the chick could not from the platform jump onto the edge of the stovepipe or the top of the pen wall. The only means of exit was to go up the steps to the platform, up through the stovepipe to the front wall, and then jump down.

The time-curves for chicks 90, 91, 92, 93, 94 and 95, all 2–8 days old when experimented on, follow on page 65.

The scale is the same as that in the curves of the cats and dogs. Besides these simple acts, which any average chick will accidentally hit upon and associate, there are, in the records of my preliminary study of animal intelligence, a multitude of all sorts of associations which some chicks have happened to form. Chicks have escaped from confinement by stepping on a little platform in the back of the box, by jumping up and pulling a string like that in D, by pecking at a door, by climbing up a spiral staircase and out through a hole in the wall, by doing this and then in addition walking across a ladder for a foot to another wall from which they jump down, etc. Not every chick will happen upon the right way in these cases, but the chicks who did happen upon it all formed the associations perfectly after enough trials.

The behavior of the chicks shows the same general character as that of the cats, conditioned, of course, by the different nature of the instinctive impulses. Take a chick put in T (inclined plane) for an example. When taken from the food and other chicks and dropped into the pen he shows evident signs of discomfort; he runs back and forth, peeping loudly, trying to squeeze through any openings there may be, jumping up to get over the wall, and pecking at the bars or screen, if such separate him from the other chicks. Finally, in his general running around he goes up the inclined plane a way. He may come down again, or he may go on up far enough to see over the top of the wall. If he does, he will probably go running up the rest of the way and jump down. With further trials he gains more and more of an impulse to walk up an inclined plane when he sees it, while the vain running and pecking, etc., are stamped out by the absence of any sequent pleasure. Finally, the chick goes up the plane as soon as put in. In scientific terms this history means that the chick, when confronted by loneliness and confining walls, responds by those acts which in similar conditions in nature would be likely to free him. Some one of these acts leads him to the successful act, and the resulting pleasure stamps it in. Absence of pleasure stamps all others out. The case is just the same as with dogs and cats. The time-curves are shown in Fig. 18.

Coming now to the question of differences in intelligence between the different animals, it is clear that such differences are hard to estimate accurately. The chicks are surely very much slower in forming associations and less able to tackle hard ones, but the biggest part of the difference between what they do and what the dogs and cats do is not referable so much to any difference in intelligence as to a difference in their bodily organs and instinctive impulses. As between dogs and cats, the influence of the difference in quantity of activity, in the direction of the instinctive impulses, in the versatility of the fore limb, is hard to separate from the influence of intelligence proper. The best practical tests to judge such differences in general would be differences in memory, which are very easily got at, differences in the delicacy and complexity attainable, and, of course, differences in the slope of the curves for the same association. If all these tests agreed, we should have a right to rank one animal above the other in a scale of intelligence. But this whole question of grading is, after all, not so important for comparative psychology as its popularity could lead one to think. Comparative psychology wants first of all to trace human intellection back through the phylum to its origin, and in this aim is helped little by knowing that dogs are brighter than cats, or whales than seals, or horses than cows. Further, the whole question of 'intelligence' should be resolved into particular

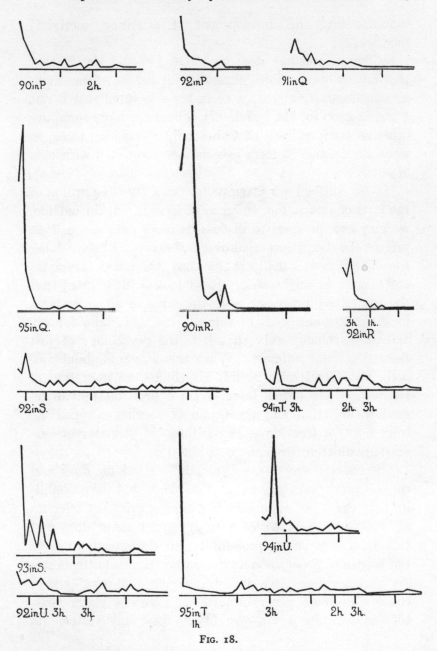

FIG. 18.

inquiries into the development of attention, activity, memory, etc.

So far as concerns dogs and cats, I should decide that the former were more generally intelligent. The main reason, however, why dogs seem to us so intelligent is not a good reason for the belief. It is because, more than any other domestic animal, they direct their attention to *us*, to what we do, and so form associations connected with acts of ours.

Having finished our attempt to give a true description of the facts of association, so far as observed from the outside, we may now progress to discuss its inner nature. A little preface about certain verbal usages is necessary before doing so. Throughout I shall use the word 'animal' or 'animals,' and the reader might fancy that I took it for granted that the associative processes were the same in all animals as in these cats and dogs of mine. Really, I claim for my animal psychology only that it is the psychology of just these particular animals. What this warrants about animals in general may be left largely to the discretion of the reader. As I shall later say, it is probable that in regard to imitation and the power of forming associations from a lot of free ideas, the anthropoid primates are essentially different from the cats and dogs.

The reasons why I say 'animals' instead of 'dogs and cats of certain ages' are two. I do think that the probability that the other mammals, barring the primates, offer no objections to the theories here advanced about dogs and cats is a very strong probability, strong enough to force the burden of proof upon any one who should, for instance, say that horse-goat psychology was not like cat-dog psychology in these general matters. I should claim that, till the contrary was shown in any case, my statements should stand for the mammalian mind in general, barring the primates. My second reason is that I hate to burden the reader with the disgusting rhetoric which would result if I had to insert particularizations and reservations at every step. The word 'animal' is too useful, rhetorically, to be sacrificed. Finally, inasmuch as most of my theorizing will be in the line of denying certain relatively high functions to animals, the evidence from cats and dogs is sufficient, for they are from among the most intelligent animals, and functions of the kind to be discussed, if absent in their case, are probably absent from the others.

REASONING OR INFERENCE

The first great question is whether or not animals are ever led to do any of their acts by reasoning. Do they ever conclude from inference that a certain act will produce a certain desired result, and so do it? The best opinion has been that they do not. The best interpretation of even the most extraordinary performances of animals has been that they were the result of accident and association or imitation. But it has after all been only opinion and interpretation, and the opposite theory persistently reappears in the literature of the subject. So, although it is in a way superfluous to give the *coup de grâce* to the despised theory that animals reason, I think it is worth while to settle this question once for all.

The great support of those who do claim for animals the ability to infer has been their wonderful performances which resemble our own. These could not, they claim, have happened by accident. No animal could learn to open a latched gate by accident. The whole substance of the argument vanishes if, as a matter of fact, animals do learn those things by accident. *They certainly do.* In this investigation choice was made of the intelligent performances described by Romanes in the following passages. I shall quote at some length because these passages give an admirable illustration of an attitude of investigation which this research will, I hope, render impossible for any scientist in the future. Speaking of the general intelligence of cats, Romanes says:

"Thus, for instance, while I have only heard of one solitary case . . . of a dog which, without tuition, divined the use of a thumb latch so as to open a closed door by jumping on the handle and depressing the thumb-piece, I have received some half-dozen instances of this display of intelligence on the part of cats. These instances are all such precise repetitions of one another that I conclude the fact to be one of tolerably ordinary occurrence among cats, while it is certainly rare among dogs. I may add that my own coachman once had a cat which, certainly without tuition, learnt thus to open a door that led into the stables from a yard into which looked some of the windows of the house. Standing at these windows when the cat did not see me, I have many times witnessed her *modus operandi.* Walking up to the door with a most matter-of-course kind of air, she used to spring at the half hoop handle just below the thumb latch. Holding on to the bottom of this half-hoop with one fore paw, she then raised the other to the thumb piece, and while depressing the latter finally with her hind legs scratched and pushed the door posts so as to open the door. . . .

"Of course in all such cases the cats must have previously observed that the doors are opened by persons placing their hands upon the handles and, having observed this, the animals act by what may be strictly termed rational imitation. But it should be observed that the process as a whole is something more than imitative. For not only would observation alone be scarcely enough (within any limits of thoughtful reflection that it would be reasonable to ascribe to an animal) to enable a cat upon the ground to distinguish that the essential part of the process consists not in grasping the handle, but in depressing the latch; but the cat certainly never saw any one, after having depressed the latch, pushing the door posts with his legs; and that this pushing action is due to an originally deliberate intention of opening the door, and not to having accidentally found this action to assist the process, is shown by one of the cases communicated to me; for in this case, my correspondent says, 'the door was not a loose-fitting one, by any means, and I was surprised that by the force of one hind leg she should have been able to push it open after unlatching it.' Hence we can only conclude that the cats in such cases have a very definite idea as to the mechanical properties of a door: they know that to make it open, even when unlatched, it requires to be *pushed* — a very different thing from trying to imitate any particular action which they may see to be performed for the same purpose by man. The whole psychological process, therefore, implied by the fact of a cat opening a door in this way is really most complex. First the animal must have observed that the door is opened by the hand grasping the handle and moving the latch. Next she must reason, by 'the logic of feelings' — 'If a hand can do it, why not a paw?' Then strongly moved by this idea she makes the first trial. The steps which follow have not been observed, so we cannot certainly say whether she learns by a succession of trials that depression of the thumb piece constitutes the essential part of the process, or, perhaps more probably, that her initial observations supplied her with the idea of clicking the thumb piece. But, however this may be, it is certain that the pushing with the hind feet after depressing the latch must be due to adaptive reasoning unassisted by observation; and only by the concerted action of all her limbs in the performance of a highly complex and most unnatural movement is her final purpose attained." (Animal Intelligence, pp. 420–422.)

A page or two later we find a less ponderous account of a cat's success in turning aside a button and so opening a window : —

"At Parara, the residence of Parker Bowman, Esq., a full-grown cat was one day accidentally locked up in a room without any other outlet than a small window, moving on hinges, and kept shut by means of a swivel. Not long afterwards the window was found open and the cat gone. This having happened several times, it was at last found that the cat jumped upon the window sill, placed her fore paws as high as she could reach against the side, deliberately reached with one over to the swivel, moved it from its horizontal to a vertical position, and then, leaning with her whole weight against the window, swung it open and escaped." (Animal Intelligence, p. 425.)

A description has already been given on page 31 of the small box (C), whose door fell open when the button was turned, and also of a large box (CC) for the dogs, with a similar door. The thumb-latch experiment was carried on with the same box (G) for both cats and dogs, but the door was arranged so that a greater force (1.3 kilograms) was required in the case of the dogs. It will be remembered that the latch was so fixed that if the thumb piece were pressed down, without contemporaneous outward pressure of the door, the latch bar would merely drop back into its catch as soon as the paw was taken off the door. If, however, the door were pushed outward, the latch bar, being pressed closely against the outer edge of its catch, would, if lifted, be likely to fall outside it and so permit the door to open if then or later sufficient pressure were exerted. Eight cats (Nos. 1, 2, 3, 4, 5, 6, 7 and 13) were, one at a time, left in this thumb-latch box. All exhibited the customary instinctive clawings and squeezings and bitings. Out of the eight all succeeded in the course of their vigorous struggles in pressing down the thumb piece, so that if the door had been free to swing open, they could have escaped. Six succeeded in pushing both thumb-piece down and door out, so that the bar did not fall back into its place. Of these five succeeded in also later pushing the door open, so that they escaped and got the fish outside. Of these, three, after repeated trials, associated the complicated movements required with the sight of the interior of the box so firmly that they attacked the thumb latch the moment they were put in. The history of the formation of the association in the case of 3 and of 4 is shown in the curves in Figs. 6 and 7. In the case of 13 the exact times were not taken. The combination of accidents required was enough to make No. 1 and No. 6 take a long time to get out. Consequently, weariness and failure inhibited their impulses to claw, climb, etc., more than the rare pleasure from getting out strengthened them, and they failed to form the association. Like the

TABLE 3

No. 1.	No. 6.
13.00 F	17.50
9.30	3.30
1.40	9.00
.50	2.10
15.00	1.45
6.00 F	1.55
14.00	13.00
20.00 F	5.00
4.30	2.30
20.00 F	15.00
20.00 F	10.00 F
15.00 F	5.00
60.00 F	15.00 F
	10.00 F
	10.00 F

cats who utterly failed to get out, they finally ceased to try when put in. The history of their efforts is as in Table 3 : the figures in the columns represent the time (in minutes and seconds) the animal was in the box before escaping or before being taken out if he failed to escape. Cases of failure are designated by an F after the figures. Double lines represent an interval of twenty-four hours.

It should be noted that, although cats 3 and 4 had had some experience in getting out of boxes by clawing at loops and turning buttons, they had never had anything at all like a thumb latch to claw at, nor had they ever seen the door opened by its use, nor did they even have any experience of the fact that the part of the box where the thumb piece was was the door. And we may insert here, what will be stated more fully later, that there was displayed no observation of the surroundings or deliberation upon them. It was just a mad scramble to get out.

Three dogs (1, 2 and 3) were given a chance to liberate themselves from this same box. 2 and 3, who were rather inactive, failed to even push the thumb piece down. No. 1, who was very active, did push it down at the same time that she happened to be pushing against the door. She repeated this and formed the association as shown in the curve on page 60. She had had experience only of escaping by pulling a loop of string.

Out of 6 cats who were put in the box whose door opened by a button, not one failed, in the course of its impulsive activity, to push the button around. Sometimes it was clawed to one side from below; sometimes vigorous pressure on the top turned it around; sometimes it was pushed up by the nose. No cat who was given repeated trials failed to form a perfect association between the sight of the interior of that box and the proper movements. Some of these cats had been in other boxes where pulling a loop of string liberated them, 3 and 4 had had considerable experience with the boxes and probably had acquired a general tendency to claw at loose objects. 10, 11 and 12 had never been in *any box* before. The curves are on pages 41 and 43.

Of two dogs, one, when placed in a similar but larger box, succeeded in hitting the button in such a way as to let the door open, and formed a permanent association, as shown by the curves on page 41. No one who had seen the behavior of these animals when trying to escape could doubt that their actions were directed by instinctive impulses, not by rational observation. It is then absolutely sure that a dog or cat *can* open a door closed by a thumb latch or button, merely by the accidental success of its natural impulses. If *all* cats, when hungry and in a *small* box, will accidentally push the button that holds the door, an *occasional* cat in a *large* room may very well do the same. If three cats out of eight will accidentally press down a thumb piece and push open a small door, three cats out of a thousand may very well open doors or gates in the same way.

But besides thus depriving of their value the facts which these theorizers offer as evidence, we may, by a careful examination of the method of formation of these associations as it is shown in the time-curves, gain positive evidence that no power of inference was present in the subjects of the experiments. Surely if 1 and 6 had possessed any power of inference, they would not have failed to get out after having done so several times. Yet they did. (See p. 71.) If they had once even, much less if they had six or eight times, inferred what was to be done, they should have made the inference the seventh or ninth time. And if there were in these animals any power of inference, however rudimentary, however sporadic, however dim, there should have appeared among the multitude some cases where an animal, seeing through the situation, knows the proper act, does it, and from then on does it immediately upon being confronted with the situation. There ought, that is, to be a sudden vertical descent in the time-curve. Of course, where the act resulting from the impulse is very simple, very obvious, and very clearly defined, a single experience may make the association perfect, and we may have an abrupt descent in the time-curve without needing to suppose inference. But if in a complex act, a series of acts or an ill-defined act, one found such a sudden consummation in the associative process, one might very well claim that reason was at work. Now, the scores of cases recorded show no such phenomena. The cat does not look over the situation, much less *think* it over, and then decide what to do. It bursts out at once into the activities which instinct and experience have settled on as suitable reactions to the situation '*confinement when hungry with food outside.*' It does not ever in the course of its successes realize that such an act brings food and therefore decide to do it and thenceforth do it immediately from *decision* instead of from impulse. The one impulse, out of many accidental ones, which leads to pleasure, becomes strengthened and stamped in thereby, and more and more firmly associated with the sense-impression of that box's interior. Accordingly it is sooner and sooner fulfilled. Futile impulses are gradually stamped out. The gradual slope of the time-curve, then, shows the absence of reasoning. They represent the wearing smooth of a path in the brain, not the decisions of a rational consciousness.

In a later discussion of imitation further evidence that animals do not reason will appear. For the present, suffice it to say, that a dog, or cat, or chick, who does not in his own impulsive activity learn to escape from a box by pulling the proper loop, or stepping on a platform, or pecking at a door, will not learn it from seeing his fellows do so. They are incapable of even the inference (if the process may be dignified by that name) that what gives another food will give it to them also. So, also, it will be later seen that an

animal cannot learn an act by being put through it. For
instance, a cat who fails to push down a thumb piece and
push out the door cannot be taught by having one take
its paw and press the thumb piece down with it. This
could be learned by a certain type of associative process
without inference. *Were there inference, it surely would be
learned.*

Finally, attention may be called to the curves which
show the way that the animal mind deals with a series
of acts (*e.g.* curves for G, J, K, L and O, found on pages 45
to 55 and 60.) Were there any reasoning the animals ought
early to master the method of escape in these cases (see
descriptions on pages 31 to 34) so as to do the several
acts in order, and not to repeat one after doing it once, or
else ought utterly to fail to master the thing. But, in all
these experiments, where there was every motive for the
use of any reasoning faculty, if such existed, where the animals literally lived by their intellectual powers, one finds
no sign of abstraction, or inference, or judgment.

So far I have only given facts which are quite uninfluenced
by any possible incompetence or prejudice of the observer.
These alone seem to disprove the existence of any rational
faculty in the subjects experimented on. I may add that
my observations of all the conduct of all these animals
during the months spent with them, failed to find any act
that even *seemed* due to reasoning. I should claim that this
quarrel ought now to be dropped for good and all,—that
investigation ought to be directed along more sensible and
profitable lines. I should claim that the psychologist who
studies dogs and cats in order to defend this 'reason' theory
is on a level with a zoölogist who should study fishes with
a view to supporting the thesis that they possessed clawed
digits. The rest of this account will deal with more prom-

ising problems, of which the first, and not the least important, concerns the facts and theories of *imitation*.

IMITATION

To the question, 'Do animals imitate?' science has uniformly answered, 'Yes.' But so long as the question is left in this general form, no correct answer to it is possible. It will be seen, from the results of numerous experiments soon to be described, that imitation of a certain sort is not possible for animals, and before entering upon that description it will be helpful to differentiate this matter of imitation into several varieties or aspects. The presence of some sorts of imitation does not imply that of other sorts.

There are, to begin with, the well-known phenomena presented by the imitative birds. The power is extended widely, ranging from the parrot who knows a hundred or more articulate sounds to the sparrow whom a patient shoemaker taught to get through a tune. Now, if a bird really gets a sound in his mind from hearing it and sets out forthwith to imitate it, as mocking birds are said at times to do, it is a mystery and deserves closest study. If a bird, out of a lot of random noises that it makes, chooses those for repetition which are like sounds that he has heard, it is again a mystery *why*, though not as in the previous case a mystery *how*, he does it. The important fact for our purpose is that, though the imitation of sounds is so habitual, there does not appear to be any marked general imitative tendency in these birds. There is no proof that parrots do muscular acts from having seen other parrots do them. But this should be studied. At any rate, until we know what sort of sounds birds imitate, what circumstances or emotional attitudes these are connected with, how they learn them and, above all, whether there is in birds which repeat sounds any tendency to imitate in other lines, we cannot, it seems to me, connect these phenomena with anything found in the mammals or use them to advantage in a discussion of animal imitation as the forerunner of human. In what follows they will be left out of account, will be regarded as a specialization removed from the general course of mental development, just as the feathers or right aortic arch of birds are particular specializations of no consequence for the physical development of mammals. For us, henceforth, imitation will mean imitation minus the phenomena of imitative birds.

There are also certain pseudo-imitative or semi-imitative phenomena which ought to be considered by themselves. For example, the rapid loss of the fear of railroad trains or telegraph wires among birds, the rapid acquisition of arboreal habits among Australian rodents, the use of proper feeding grounds, etc., may be held to be due to imitation. The young animal stays with or follows its mother from a specific instinct to keep near that particular object, to wit, its mother. It may thus learn to stay near trains, or scramble up trees, or feed at certain places and on certain plants. Actions due to following pure and simple may thus simulate imitation. Other groups of acts which now seem truly imitative may be indirect fruits of some one instinct. This must be kept in mind when one estimates the supposed imitation of parents by young. Further, it is certain that in the case of the chick, where early animal life has been carefully observed, instinct and individual experience between them rob imitation of practically all its supposed influence. Chicks get along without a mother very well. Yet no mother takes more care of her children than the hen. Care in other cases, then, need not mean instruction through imitation.

These considerations may prevent an unreserved acceptance of the common view that young animals get a great number of their useful habits from imitation, but I do not expect or desire them to lead to its summary rejection. I should not now myself reject it, though I think it quite possible that more investigation and experiment may finally reduce all the phenomena of so-called imitation of parents by young to the level of indirect results of instinctive acts.

Another special department of imitation may be at least vaguely marked off : namely, apparent imitation of certain limited sorts of acts which are somewhat frequent in the animal's life. An example will do better than further definition.

Some sheep were being driven on board ship one at a time. In the course of their progress they had to jump over a hurdle. On this being removed before all had passed it, the next sheep was seen to jump as if to get over a hurdle, and so on for five or six, apparently sure evidence that they imitated the action, each of the one in front. Now, it is again possible that among gregarious animals there may be elaborate connections in the nervous system which allow the sight of certain particular acts in another animal to arouse the innervation leading to those acts, but that these connections are *limited*. The reactions on this view are specific responses to definite signals, comparable to any other instinctive or associational reaction. The sheep jumps when he sees the other sheep jump, not because of a general ability to do what he sees done, but because he is furnished with the instinct to jump at such a sight, or because his experience of following the flock over boulders

and brooks and walls has got him into the habit of jumping
at the spot where he sees one ahead of him jump; and so
he jumps even though no obstacle be in his way. If due
to instinct, the only peculiarity of such a reaction would be
that the sense-impression calling forth the act would be the
same act as done by another. If due to experience, there
would be an exact correspondence to the frequent acts
called forth *originally* by several elements in a sense-impression, one of which is essential, and done *afterwards*
when only the *non-essentials* are present. These two
possibilities have not been sufficiently realized, yet they
may contain the truth. On the other hand, these limited
acts may be the primitive, sporadic beginnings of the
general imitative faculty which we find in man. To this
general faculty we may now turn, having cleared away
some of the more doubtful phenomena which have shared
its name.

It should be kept in mind that an imitative act may be
performed quite unthinkingly, as when a man in the mob
shouts what the others shout or claps when the others clap;
may be done from an inference that since A by doing X makes
pleasure for himself, I by doing X may get pleasure for myself; may, lastly, be done from what may be called a transferred association. This process is the one of interest in
connection with our general topic, and most of my experiments on imitation were directed to the investigation
of it. Its nature is simple. One sees the following sequence: 'A turning a faucet, A getting a drink.' If one
can free this association from its narrow confinement to A,
so as to get from it the association, 'impulse to turn faucet,
me getting a drink,' one will surely, if thirsty, turn the
faucet, though he had never done so before. If one can
from an act witnessed learn to do the act, he in some way

makes use of the sequence seen, transfers the process to himself; in the common human sense of the word, he *imitates*. This kind of imitation is surely common in human life. It may be apparent in ontogeny before any power of inference is shown. After that power does appear, it still retains a wide scope, and teaches us a majority, perhaps, of the ordinary accomplishments of our practical life.

Now, as the writers of books about animal intelligence have not differentiated this meaning from the other possible ones, it is impossible to say surely that they have uniformly credited it to animals, and it is profitless to catalogue here their vague statements. Many opposers of the 'reason' theory have presupposed such a process and used it to replace reason as the cause of some intelligent performances. The upholders of the reason theory have customarily recognized such a process and claimed to have discounted it in their explanations of the various anecdotes. So we found Mr. Romanes, in the passage quoted, discussing the possibility that such an imitative process, without reason, could account for the facts. In his chapter on Imitation in 'Habit and Instinct,' Principal C. Lloyd Morgan, the sanest writer on comparative psychology, seems to accept imitation of this sort as a fact, though he could, if attacked, explain most of his illustrations by the simple forms. The fact is, as was said before, that no one has analyzed or systematized the phenomena, and so one cannot find clear, decisive statements to quote.

At any rate, whether previous authorities have agreed that such a process is present or not, it is worth while to tackle the question; and the formation of associations by imitation, if it occurs, is an important division of the formation of associations in general. The experiments and their results may now be described.

IMITATION IN CHICKS

No. 64 learned to get out of a certain pen (16 × 10 inches) by crawling under the wire screening at a certain spot. There was also a chance to get out by walking up an inclined plane and then jumping down. No. 66 was put in with 64. After 9 minutes 20 seconds, 66 went out by the inclined plane, although 64 had in the meantime crawled out under the screen 9 times. (As soon as he got out and ate a little

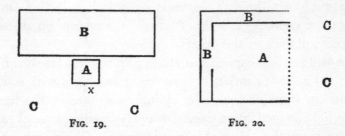

FIG. 19.   FIG. 20.

he was put back.) It was impossible to judge how many of these times 66 really saw 64 do this. He was looking in that direction 5 of the times. So also, in three more trials, 66 used the inclined plane, though 64 crawled under each time. 67 was then tried. In 4 minutes 10 seconds, he crawled under, 64 having done so twice. Being then put in *alone*, he, without the chance to imitate, still crawled under. So probably he went under *when with 64* not by imitation but by accident, just as 64 had learned the thing himself.

The accompanying figure (19) shows the apparatus used in the next experiment. A represents the top of a box (5 × 4 inches), 13 inches above the level of the floor C. On the floor C were the chicks and food. B is the top of a box 10 inches high. Around the edges of A except the one next B a wire screen was placed, and 65 was repeatedly put upon A until he learned to go quickly back to C *via* B. Then the screen was bent outward at X so that a chick could barely squeeze through and down (A to C). Eleven chicks were then one at a time placed on A with 65. In every case but one they went A–C. In the case of the chick (75) who went A–B–C, there could have been no imitation, for he went down *before* 65 did. One other went through the hole before 65 went to B. The remaining nine all had a chance to imitate 65 and to save the uncomfortable struggle to get through the hole, 65 going A–B–C 8 times before 68 went A–C, 2 times when with 66 and 76, once in the case of each of the others.

In still another experiment the apparatus was (as shown in Fig. 20) a pen 14 inches square, 10 inches high, with a wire screen in front and a hole $3\frac{1}{2}$ inches square in the back. This hole opened into a passageway (B) leading around to C, where were the other chicks and food. Chicks who had failed, when put in alone, to find the way out, were put in with other chicks who had learned the way, to see if by seeing them go out they would learn the way. Chick 70 was given 4 trials alone, being left in the box 76 minutes all told. He was then given 9 trials (165 minutes) with another chick who went out *via* B 36 times. 70 failed to follow him on any occasion. The trials were all given in the course of two days. Chick 73 failed in 1 trial (12 minutes) to get out of himself, and was then given 4 trials (94 minutes) with another chick who went out *via* B 33 times. In this experiment, as in all others reported, sure evidence that the animals wanted to get out, was afforded by their persistent peckings and jumpings at the screen or bars that stood between them and C. Chick 72, after 8 unsuccessful trials alone (41 minutes), was given 8 trials with a chance to imitate. After the other chick had gone out 44 times, 72 *did go out.* He did not follow the other but went 20 seconds later. It depends upon one's general opinion whether one shall attribute this one case out of three to accident or imitation.

I also took two chicks, one of whom learned to escape from A (in Fig. 19) by going to B and jumping down the side to the *right* of A, the other of whom learned to jump down the side to the *left*, and placed them together upon A. Each took his own course uninfluenced by the other in 10 trials.

Chicks were also tried in several pens where there was only one possible way of escape to see if they would learn it *more quickly* when another chick did the thing several times before their eyes. The method was to give some chicks their first trial with an imitation possibility and their second without, while others were given their first trial without and their second with. If the ratio of the average time of the first trial to the average time of the second is smaller in the first class than it is in the second class, we may find evidence of this sort of influence by imitation. Though imitation may not be able to make an animal *do* what he would otherwise *not do*, it may make him do *quicker* a thing he would have done sooner or later any way. As a fact the ratio is *much larger.* This is due to the fact that a chick, when in a pen with another chick, is not afflicted by the discomfort of loneliness, and so does not try so hard to get out. So the other chick, who is continually being put in with him to teach him the way out, really prolongs his stay in. This factor destroys the value of these quantitative experiments, and I do not insist upon them as evidence against imitation, though they certainly offer none for it. I do not give descriptions of the apparatus used in these experiments or a detailed enumeration of the results, because in this discussion we are not dealing primarily with imitation as a slight general factor in forming experience, but as a definite associational process in the mind. The utter absence of imitation in this limited sense is apparently demonstrated by the results of the following experiments.

V was a box 16 × 12 × 8½, with the front made of wire screening and at the left end a little door held by a bolt but in such a way that a sharp peck at the top of the door would force it open.

W was a box of similar size, with a door in the same place fixed so that it was opened by raising a bolt. To this bolt was tied a string which went up over the top of the edge of the box and back across the box, as in D. By jumping up and coming down with the head over this thread, the bolt would be pulled up. The thread was 8½ inches above the floor.

X was a box of similar size, with door, bolt and string likewise. But here the string continued round a pulley at the back down to a platform in the corner of the box. By stepping on the platform the door was opened.

Y was a box 12 × 8 × 8½, with a door in the middle of the front, which I myself opened when a chick pecked at a tack which hung against the front of the box 1½ inches above the top of the door.

These different acts, pecking at a door, jumping up and with the neck pulling down a string, stepping on a platform, and pecking at a tack, were the ones which various chicks were given a chance to imitate. The chicks used were from 16 to 30 days old. The method of experiment was to put a chick in, leave him 60 to 80 seconds, then put in another who knew the act, and on his performing it, to let both escape. No cases were counted unless the imitator apparently saw the other do the thing. After about ten such chances to learn the act, the imitator was left in alone for ten minutes. The following table gives the results. The

imitators, of course, had previously failed to form the association of themselves.   F denotes failure to perform the act :

TABLE 4

CHICK	ACT	No. TIMES SAW	TIME IN WHICH FAILED	FINAL TIME
84	V	38	45.00 F	15.00 F
85	V	30	30.00 F	10.00 F
86	V	44	55.00 F	15.00 F
87	V	26	35.00 F	15.00 F
80	W	54	60.00 F	15.00 F
81	W	40	45.00 F	15.00 F
87	W	27	30.00 F	10.00 F
81	X	18	20.00 F	10.00 F
82	X	21	20.00 F	8.40 *Did*
83	X	33	35.00 F	15.00 F
84	X	46	55.00 F	15.00 F
84	Y	45	55.00 F	15.00 F
83	Y	29	35.00 F	15.00 F

Thus out of all these cases only one did the act in spite of
the ample chance for imitation.   I have no hesitation in
declaring 82's act in stepping on the platform the result
of mere accident, and am sure that any one who had watched
the experiments would agree.

IMITATION IN CATS

By reference to the previous descriptions of apparatus, it
will be seen that box D was arranged with two compart-
ments, separated by a wire screen.   The larger of these had
a front of wooden bars with a door which fell open when a
string stretched across the top was bitten or clawed down.
The smaller was closed by boards on three sides and by the
wire screen on the fourth.   Through the screen a cat within
could see the one to be imitated pull the string, go out

through the door thus opened and eat the fish outside. When put in this compartment, the top being covered by a large box, a cat soon gave up efforts to claw through the screen, quieted down and watched more or less the proceedings going on in the other compartment. Thus this apparatus could be used to test the power of imitation. A cat who had no experience with the means of escape from the large compartment was put in the closed one; another cat, who would do it readily, was allowed to go through the performance of pulling the string, going out, and eating the fish. Record was made of the number of times he did so and of the number of times the imitator had his eyes clearly fixed on him. These were called 'times seen.' Cases where the imitator was looking in the general direction of the 'imitatee' and might very well have seen him and probably did, were marked 'doubtful.' In the remaining cases the cat did not see what was done by his instructor. After the imitatee had done the thing a number of times, the other was put in the big compartment alone, and the time it took him before pulling the string was noted and his general behavior closely observed. If he failed in 5 or 10 or 15 minutes to do so, he was released and not fed. This entire experiment was repeated a number of times. From the times taken by the imitator to escape and from observation of the way that he did it, we can decide whether imitation played any part. The history of several cases are given in the following tables. In the first column are given the lengths of time that the imitator was shut up in the box watching the imitatee. In the second column is the number of times that the latter did the trick. In the third and fourth are the times that the imitator surely and possibly saw it done, while in the last is given the time that, when tried alone, the imitator took to pull the string, or if he failed, the time he was in the box trying to get out. Times are in minutes and seconds, failures denoted by F :

TABLE 5 (a)

		No. 7 IMITATING No. 2			
	Time Watching	No. of times 2 did	No. of times 7 saw	No. of times Doubtful	Time of 7 when alone
	1000.	11	3	5	
After 48 Hours	11.00	10	4	2	
	12.00	20	4	13	10.00 F
					1.00 [1]
After 24 Hours	8.00	20	6	11	3.30
					10.00 F
	13.00	25	8	12	20.00 F
After 24 Hours	9.00	20	4	11	10.00 F
After 24 Hours	12.00	35	5	21	30.00 F
After 2 Hours	10.00	25	3	8	25.00 F
After 24 Hours	15.00	35	6	21	20.00 F
After 24 Hours	6.00	20	0	7	10.00 F
Total times surely and possibly seen, -			43	111	

TABLE 5 (b)

		No. 5 IMITATING No. 2			
	Time Watching	No. of times 2 did	No. of times 5 saw	No. of times Doubtful	Time of 5 when alone
	12.00	15	3	8	5.00 F
After 2 Hours	10.00	8	4	4	
After 24 Hours	5.00	5	0	3	
After 1 Hour	14.00	10	5	3	10.00 F
After 1 Hour	13.00	22	7	11	10.00 F
After 24 Hours	7.00	15	3	8	5.00 F
After 48 Hours	18.00	20	2	9	20.00 F
After 24 Hours	14.00	20	2	10	30.00 F
After 24 Hours	10.00	20	7	12	20.00 F
Total times surely and possibly seen, -			33	68	

[1] No. 7 hit the string in his general struggling, apparently utterly without design. He did not realize that the door was open till, two seconds after it had fallen, he happened to look that way.

TABLE 5 (c)

	Time Watching	No. 6 IMITATING No. 2			Time of 6 when alone
		No. of times 2 did	No. of times 6 saw	No. of times Doubtful	
	12.00	30	0	19	1.10[1]
After 48 Hours	11.00	30	0	11	9.30
After 72 Hours	10.00	30	0	15	3.00
After 72 Hours	6.00	20	3	7	1.50
After 24 Hours	9.00	30	1	13	10.00 F
After 24 Hours	10.00	30	6	9	10.00 F
After 24 Hours	10.00	30	1	8	9.40
Total times surely and possibly seen, -		11		82	

TABLE 5 (d)

		No. 3 IMITATING No. 2			
	8.00	30	2	19	3.30[2]
					3.30
After 48 Hours	10.00	30	2	14	.20
					.20
After 72 Hours	10.00	30	2	8	.18
					.08
Total times surely and possibly seen, -		6		41	

Before entering upon a discussion of the facts shown by these tables, we must describe the behavior of the imitators, when, after seeing 2 pull the string, they were put in alone. In the opinion of the present observer there was not the

[1] No. 6, in trying to crawl out at the top of the box, put its paw in above the string. It fell down and thus pulled the string. It did not claw *at* it, and it was 16 seconds before it noticed that the door was open. In all the other times that it escaped the movement was made in the course of promiscuous scrambling, never in anything like the same way that No. 2 made it.

[2] No. 3 did not go out until 12 seconds had elapsed after it had pulled the string.

slightest difference between their behavior and that of cats
4, 10, 11, 12 and 13, who were put into the same position
without ever having seen 2 escape from it. 6, 7, 5 and 3
paid no more attention to the string than they did, but
struggled in just the same way.   No one, I am sure, who had
seen them, would have claimed that their conduct was at all
influenced by what they had seen.   When they did hit the
string the act looked just like the accidental success of the
ordinary association experiment.   But, besides these personal observations, we have in the impersonal time-records
sufficient proofs of the absence of imitation. If the animals pulled the string from having seen 2 do so, they ought
to pull it in each individual case at an approximately regular
length of time after they were put in, and presumably pretty
soon thereafter.   That is, if an association between the sight
of that string in that total situation and a certain impulse
and consequent freedom and food had been formed in their
minds by the observation of the acts of 2, they ought to pull
it *on seeing it,* and if any disturbing factor required that a
certain time should elapse before the imitative faculty got
in working order, that time ought to be somewhere near
constant.   The times were, as a fact, long and irregular in
the extreme.   Furthermore, if the successful cases were
even in part due to imitation, the times ought to decrease
the more they saw 2 do the thing.   Except with 3, they *increase* or give place to failures.   Whereas 6 and 7, if they
had been put in again immediately after their first successful trial and from then on repeatedly, would have unques-
tionably formed the association, they did not, when put in
after a further chance to increase their knowledge by imitation, do the thing as soon as before.   The case of 3 is not
here comparable to the rest because he *was* given three trials
in immediate succession.   He was a more active cat and

quicker to learn, as may be seen by comparing his time curves with those of 7, 6 and 5. That the mere speed with which he mastered this association is no sign that imitation was present may be seen by reference to the time curves of 4 and 13 (on p. 43).

Some cats were also experimented with in the following manner. They were put into a box [No. 7 into box A (O at front), No. 5 into B (O at back)] and left for from 45 to 75 seconds. Then a cat who knew the way to get out was put in, and, of course, pulled at the loop and opened the door. *Both cats then went out and both were fed.* After the cat had been given a number of such chances to learn by imitation, he was put in and left until he did the thing, or until 5 or 10 minutes elapsed. As in the preceding experiments, no change in their behavior which might signify imitation was observed. No. 7 acted exactly like 3, or 10, or 11, when put in the box, apparently forming the association by accident in just the same way. Good evidence that he did not imitate is the fact that, whereas 1 (whom he saw) pulled the loop with his teeth, 7 pulled it with his paw. 5 failed to form the association, though he saw 3 do it 8 times and probably saw him 18 times more. He did get out twice by clawing the *string* in the *front* of the box, not the *loop* in the *back*, as 3 did. These successes took place early in the experiment. After that he failed when left alone to get out at all.

Another experiment was made by a still different method. My cats were kept in a large box about 4 ft. high, the front of which was covered with poultry-yard netting. Its top was a board which could be removed. To save opening the door and letting them all loose, I was in the habit of taking them out by the top when I wanted to experiment with them. Of course the one who happened to climb up (perhaps attracted by the smell of fish on my fingers) was most likely to be taken out and experimented with and fed. Thus they formed the habit of climbing up the front of the box whenever I approached. Of three cats which I obtained at the same time, one did not after 8 or 10 days acquire this habit. Even though I held out a piece of fish through the netting, he would not climb after it. It was reasonable to suppose that imitation might overcome this sluggishness, if there were any imitation. I therefore put two cats with him and had them climb up 80 times before his eyes and get fish. He never followed or tried to follow them.

4 and 3 had been subjected to the following experiment. I would make a certain sound and after 10 seconds would go up to the cage and hold the fish out to them through the netting at the top. They would then, of course, climb up and eat it. After a while, they began to climb up upon hearing the signal (4) or before the 10 seconds were up. I then took 12 and 10, who were accustomed to going up when they saw me approach, but who had no knowledge of the fact that the signal meant anything, and gave them each a chance to imitate 3. That is, one of them would be left in the box with 3, the signal would be given, and after from 5 to 10 seconds 3 would climb up. At 10 seconds I would come up with food, and then, of course, 12 would climb up. This was repeated again and again. The question was whether imitation would lead them to form the association more quickly than they would have done alone. It did not. That when at last they did climb up before 10 seconds was past, that is, before I approached with food, it was not due to imitation, is shown by the fact that on about half of such occasions they climbed up *before 3 did*. That is, they reacted to the *signal* by *association*, not to his *movements* by *imitation*.

IMITATION IN DOGS

Here the method was not to see if imitation could arouse more quickly an act which accident was fairly likely to bring forth sooner or later, but to see if, where accident failed, imitation would succeed.

3 was found to be unable of himself to escape from box BB1, and was then given a chance to learn from watching 1. The back of box BB1 was torn off and wire netting substituted for it. Another box with open front was placed directly behind and against box BB1. No. 3, who was put in this second box, could thus see whatever took place in and in front of box BB1 (O at back, high). The record follows:—

TABLE 6 (a)

	Times 1 did	Times 3 saw	Times probably 3 saw	Time in alone
			DOG 3 IMITATING DOG 1	
	30	7	14	3.00 F
After 1 Hour	35	9	14	3.00 F
After 1 Hour	10	3	3	5.00 F
After 24 Hours	20	6	8	
	30	8	13	6.00 F
After 48 Hours	25	8	11	8.00 F
	25	6	12	6.00 F
	25	9	7	10.00 F
After 24 Hours	30	10	11	40.00 F
Total times surely and possibly seen, - 66		93		

A similar failure to imitate was observed in the case of another simple act. No. 1, as may be seen on page 60, had learned to escape from a pen about 8 by 5 feet by jumping up and biting a cord which ran from one end of the pen to the other and at the front end was tied to the bolt which held the door. Dogs 2 and 3 had failed in their accidental jumping and pawing to hit this cord, and were then given a chance to learn by seeing 1 do so, escape, and, of course, he fed. 1 always jumped in the same way, biting the cord at the same place, namely, where a loose end from a knot in it hung down 4 or 5 inches. 2 and 3 would either be tied up in the pen or left in a pen at one side. They had a perfect chance to see 1 perform his successful act. After every twenty or thirty performances by 1, 2 and 3 would be put in alone. It should be remembered that here, as also in the previous experiment and all others, the imitators certainly *wanted* to get out when thus left in alone. They struggled and jumped and pawed and bit, but they never jumped *at the cord*. Their records follow: —

TABLE 6 (b)

	Times 1 did	DOG 2 IMITATING DOG 1		
		Times 2 saw	Times Doubtful	Time 2 was in alone
	30	9	11	10.00 F
After 1 Hour	30	10	9	10.00 F
After 48 Hours	25	8	8	
After 1 Hour	10	3	4	9.00 F [1]
After 24 Hours	30	8	12	15.00 F
After 1 Hour	30	9	12	15.00 F
After 48 Hours	20	7	6	10.00 F
	20	8	7	
After 48 Hours	30	6	8	15.00 F
After 24 Hours	15	2	4	10.00 F
Total times surely and possibly seen, - 70			81	

[1] The back of the pen adjoined the elevator shaft, being separated from it by a partition 33 inches high. No. 2 heard the elevator coming up and put his paws up on the top of this partition so as to look over. In so doing he knocked the fastening of the cord at that end and opened the door. He did not turn to come out, and I shut the door again.

TABLE 6 (c)

	Times 1 did	DOG 3 IMITATING DOG 1		
		Times 3 saw	Times Doubtful	Time 3 was in alone
	30	10	10	10.00 F
After 1 Hour	30	9	10	10.00 F
After 1 Hour	15	6	4	
After 24 Hours	30	9	11	15.00 F
After 24 Hours	30	10	12	15.00 F
After 1 Hour	30	8	9	10.00 F
After 48 Hours	20	6	7	40.00 F
After 1 Hour	20	6	5	
After 48 Hours	30	8	9	15.00 F
After 24 Hours	15	3	4	20.00 F
Total times surely and possibly seen, -		75	81	

Another corroborative, though not very valuable, experiment was the following: Dog 3 had been taught for the purpose of another experiment to jump up on a box and beg when I held a piece of meat above the box. I then caused him to do this 110 times (within two days) in the presence of 1. Although 1 saw him at least 20 per cent of the times (3 was always fed each time he jumped on the box), he never tried to imitate him.

It seems sure from these experiments that the animals were unable to form an association leading to an act from having seen the other animal, or animals, perform the act in a certain situation. Thus we have further restricted the association process. Not only do animals not have associations accompanied, more or less permeated and altered, by inference and judgment; they do not have associations of the sort which may be acquired from other animals by imitation. What this implies concerning the actual mental content accompanying their acts will be seen later on. It also seems sure that we should give up imitation as an *a priori* explanation of any novel intelligent performance. To say that a dog who opens a gate, for instance, need not have reasoned it out *if he had seen another dog do the same thing,* is to offer, instead of one false explanation, another equally false. Imitation in any form is too doubtful a factor to be presupposed without evidence. And if a general imitative faculty is not sufficiently developed to succeed with such simple acts as those of the experiments quoted, it must be confessed that the faculty is in these higher mammals still rudimentary and capable of influencing to only the most simple and habitual acts, or else that for some reason its sphere of influence is limited to a certain class of acts, possessed of some *qualitative difference* other than mere simplicity, which renders them imitable. The latter view seems a hard one to reconcile with a sound psychology of imitation or association at present, without resorting to instinct. Unless a certain class of acts are by the innate mental make-up especially tender to the influence of imitation, the theory fails to find good psychological ground to stand on. The former view may very well be true. But in any case the burden of proof would now seem to rest upon the adherents to imitation; the promising attitude would seem to be one which went without imitation as long as it could, and that is, of course, until it surely found it present.

Returning to imitation considered in its human aspect, to imitation as a transferred association in particular, we find that here our analytical study of the animal mind promises important contributions to general comparative psychology. If it is true, and there has been no disagreement about it, that the primates do imitate acts of such novelty and complexity that only this out-and-out kind of imitation can explain the fact, we have located one great advance in mental development. Till the primates we get practically nothing but instincts and individual acquirement through impulsive trial and error. Among the primates we get also acquisition by imitation, one form of the increase of mental equipment by tradition. The child may learn from the parent quickly without the tiresome process of seeing for himself. The less active and less curious may share the progress of their superiors. The brain whose impulses hitherto could only be dislodged by specific sense-impressions may now have any impulse set agoing by the sight of the movement to which it corresponds.

All this on the common supposition that the primates *do* imitate, that a monkey in the place of these cats and dogs *would* have pulled the string. My apology for leaving the matter in this way without experiments of my own is that the monkey which I procured for just this purpose failed in two months to become tame enough to be thus experimented on. Accurate information about the nature and extent of imitation among the primates should be the first aim of further work in comparative psychology, and will be sought by the present writer as soon as he can get subjects fit for experiments.

In a questionnaire which was sent to fifteen animal trainers, the following questions were asked: —

1. "If one dog was in the habit of 'begging' to get food and another dog saw him do it ten or twenty times, would the second dog then beg himself?"

2. "In general is it easier for you to teach a cat or dog a trick if he has seen another do it?"

3. "In general do cats imitate each other? Do dogs? Do monkeys?"

4. "Give reasons for your opinion, and please write all the reasons you have."

Five gentlemen (Messrs. R. C. Carlisle, C. L. Edwards, V. P. Wormwood, H. S. Maguire and W. E. Burke) courteously responded to my questionnaire. All are trainers of acknowledged reputation. To these questions on imitation four replied.

To the first question we find the following answers: (a) "Most dogs would." (b) "Yes; he will very likely do it. He will try and imitate the other dog *generally*." (c) "If a young dog with the mother, it would be very apt to. . . . With older dogs, it would depend very much upon circumstances." (d) "He would not."

To 2 the answers were: (a) "Very much easier." (b) "It is always easier if they see another one do it often." (c) "This would also depend on certain conditions. In teaching to jump out of a box and in again, seeing another might help, but in teaching something very difficult, I do not think it would be the case." (d) "It is not."

To 3 the answers were: (a) "Yes. Some. More than either dogs or cats." (b) "Yes. Yes. Yes." (c) "In certain things, yes; mostly in those things which are in compliance to the laws of their own nature." (d) "No. No. Yes, they are born imitators."

The only definite answer to question 4 was: "Take a dog or cat and close them up in a room and go in and out several times, and you will find that they will go to the door and stand up on their hind legs with front paws on the door knob and try to open the door to get out. I could also give you a hundred more such reasons." This was given by (b).

The replies to a test question, however, go to show that these opinions regarding imitation may be mistaken. Question 8 was: "If you wanted to teach a cat to get out of a cage by opening an ordinary thumb latch and then pushing the door, would you take the cat's paw and push down the thumb piece with it and then push the door open with the

paw, or would you just leave the cat inside until it learned
the trick itself?" The second is certainly the better way,
as will be seen in a later part of this paper, and pushing the
latch with the cat's paw has absolutely no beneficial influence on the formation of the association, yet (*a*) and (*b*)
both chose the first way, and (*c*) answered ambiguously.
Further, the only reason given is, of course, no reason at all.
It proves too much, for if there were such imitation as that,
my cats and dogs would surely have done the far simpler
things required of them. I cannot find that trainers
make any practical use of imitation in teaching animals
tricks, and on the whole I think these replies leave the matter just where it was before. They are mere opinions —
not records of observed facts. It seems arrogant and may
seem to some unjustifiable thus to discard testimony, to
stick to a theory based on one's own experiments in the face
of these opinions. If I had wished to gain applause and
avoid adverse criticism, I would have abstained from up-
holding the radical view of the preceding pages. At times
it seems incredible to me that the results of my experiments should embody the truth of the matter, that there
should be no imitation. The theory based on them seems,
even to me, too radical, too novel. It seems highly improbable that I should be right and all the others wrong. But I
cannot avoid the responsibility of giving what seems to my
judgment the most probable explanation of the results of
the experiments; and that is the radical explanation already given.

THE MENTAL FACT IN ASSOCIATION

It is now time to put the question as to just what is in an
animal's mind when, having profited by numerous experi-

ences, he has formed the association and does the proper act when put in a certain box. The commonly accepted view of the mental fact then present is that the sight of the inside of the box reminds the animal of his *previous pleasant experience after escape* and *of the movements* which he made which were immediately followed by and so associated with that escape. It has been taken for granted that *if the animal remembered the pleasant experience and remembered the movement, he would make the movement.* It has been assumed that the association was *an association of ideas;* that when one of the ideas was of a movement the animal was capable of making the movement. So, for example, Morgan says, in the 'Introduction to Comparative Psychology': "If a chick takes a ladybird in its beak forty times and each time finds it nasty, this is of no practical value to the bird unless the sight of the insect suggests *the nasty taste*" (p. 90).

Again, on page 92, Morgan says, "*A race after the ball* had been suggested through the channel of olfactory sensations." Also, on page 86 ". . . the visual impression suggested the idea or representation of unpleasant gustatory experience." The attitude is brought out more completely in a longer passage on page 118: "On one of our first ascents one of them put up a young coney, and they both gave chase. Subsequently they always hurried on to this spot, and, though they never saw another coney there, reiterated disappointment did not efface *the memory of that first chase*, or so it seemed." That is, according to Morgan, the dogs thought of the chase and its pleasure, on nearing the spot where it had occurred, and so hurried on. On page 148 of 'Habit and Instinct,' we read, "Ducklings so thoroughly associated water with the sight of their tin that they tried to drink from it and wash in it when it was empty, nor did they desist for some minutes," and this with other similar phenomena is attributed to the 'association by contiguity' of human psychology.

From these quotations it seems fairly sure that if we should ask Mr. Morgan, who is our best comparative psychologist, what took place in the mind of one of these cats of our experiments during the performance of one of the 'tricks' he would reply: "The cat performs the act because of the association of ideas. He is reminded by the sight of the box and loop of his experience of pulling that loop and of eating fish outside. So he goes and pulls it again." This view has stood unchallenged, but its implication is false. It implies that an animal, whenever it thinks of an act, can supply an *impulse to do* the act. It takes for granted that the performance of a cat who gets out of a box is mentally like that of a man who thinks of going down street or of writing a letter and then does it. The mental process is not alike in the two cases, for animals can *not* provide the impulse to *do* whatever act they think *of*. *No cat can form an association leading to an act unless there is included in the association an impulse of its own which leads to the act.* There is no general storehouse from which the impulse may be supplied after the association is formed.

Before describing the experiments which justify these statements, it will be worth while to recall the somewhat obvious facts about the composition of one of these associations.   There might be in an association, such as is formed after experience with one of our boxes, the following elements: —

1. Sense-impression of the interior of the box, etc.
2. (*a*) Discomfort and (*b*) desire to get out.
3. Representation of oneself pulling the loop.
4. Fiat comparable to the human "I'll do it."
5. The impulse which actually does it.

6. Sense-impression of oneself pulling the loop, seeing one's paw in a certain place, feeling one's body in a certain way, etc.

7. Sense-impression of going outside.

8. Sense-impression of eating, and the included pleasure.

Also between 1 and 4 we may have 9, representations of one's experience in going out, 10, of the taste of the food, etc. 6, 7 and 8 come after the act and do not influence it, of course, except in so far as they are the basis of the future 3's, 9's and 10's. About 2 we are not at present disputing. Our question is as to whether 3 or 5 is the essential thing. In human associations 3 certainly often is, and the animals have been credited with the same kind. Whatever he *thinks*, Professor Morgan surely *talks* as if 1 aroused 9 and 10 and 3 and leaves 5 to be supplied at will. We have affirmed that 5 is the essential thing, that no association without a specific 5 belonging to it and acquired by it can lead to an act. Let us look at the reasons.

A cat has been made to go into a box through the door, which is then closed. She pulls a loop and comes out and gets fish. She is made to go in by the door again, and again lets herself out. After this has happened enough times, the cat will of her own accord go into the box after eating the fish. It will be hard to keep her out. The old explanation of this would be that the cat associated the memory of being in the box with the subsequent pleasure, and therefore performed the equivalent of saying to herself, "Go to! I will go in." The thought of *being in*, they say, makes her *go in*. *The thought of being in will not make her go in.* For if, instead of pushing the cat toward the doorway or holding it there, and thus allowing it to itself give the impulse, to innervate the muscles, to walk in, you shut the door first and drop the cat in through a hole in the top of the box, she will,

after escaping as many times as in the previous case, *not* go
into the box of her own accord.   She has had exactly the
same opportunity of connecting the idea of being in the box
with the subsequent pleasure.   Either a cat cannot connect
ideas, representations, at all, or she has not the power of
progressing from the thought of being in to the act of going
in.   The only difference between the first cat and the second cat is that the first cat, in the course of the experience,
has the impulse to crawl through that door, while the second
has not the impulse to crawl through the door or to drop
through that hole.   So, though you put the second cat on
the box beside the hole, she doesn't try to get into the box
through it.   The impulse is the *sine qua non* of the association.   The second cat has everything else, but cannot supply that.   These phenomena were observed in six cats, three
of which were tried by the first method, three by the
second.   Of the first three, one went in himself on the 26th
time and frequently thereafter, one on the 18th and the other
on the 37th; the two last as well as the first did that frequently in later trials.   The other three all failed to go in
themselves after 50, 60 and 75 trials, respectively.

The case of No. 7 was especially instructive, though not
among these six.   No. 7 had had some trials in which it was
put in through the door, but ordinarily in this particular
experiment was dropped in.   After about 80 trials it would
frequently exhibit the following phenomena : It would,
after eating the fish, go up to the doorway and, rushing
from it, search for fish.   The kitten was very small and
would go up into the doorway, whirl round and dash out,
all in one quick movement.   The best description of its
behavior is the paradoxical one that it went out without
going in.   The association evidently concerned what it had
done, what it had an impulse for, namely, *coming out through*

that door to get fish, not what it remembered, had a representation of.

Still more noteworthy evidence is found in the behavior of cats and dogs who were put in these boxes, left one or two minutes, and then put through the proper movement. For example, a cat would be put in B (O at back) and left two minutes. I would then put my hand in through the top of the box, take the cat's paw and with it pull down the loop. The cat would then go out and eat the fish. This would be done over and over again, and after every ten or fifteen such trials the cat would be left in alone. If in ten or twenty minutes he did not escape, he would be taken out through the top and not fed. In one series of experiments animals were taken and thus treated in boxes from which their own impulsive activity had failed to liberate them. The results, given in the table below, show that no animal who fails to perform an act in the course of his own impulsive activity will learn it by being put through it.

In these experiments some of the cats and all of the dogs but No. 1 showed no agitation or displeasure at my handling from the very start. Nor was there any in Dog 1 or the other cats after a few trials. It may also be remarked that in the trials alone which took place during and at the end of the experiment the animals without exception showed that they did not fail to perform the act from lack of a desire to get out. They all tried hard enough to get out and would surely have used the association if they had formed it.

Now, the only difference between the experiences of the animals in these experiments and their experiences in those where they let themselves out, is that here they only saw and felt themselves making the movement, whereas in the other case they also felt the impulse, gave the innervation. That, then, is the essential. It may be objected that the

Individual	Apparatus	Time in which impulsive activity failed to lead to the act	Number of times the animal was put through the movement	Time in which this experience failed to lead to the act	Time of final trial
Cat 1	F (String outside unfastened)	55.00	77	120.00	20.00
Cat 5	G (Thumb latch)	57.00	59	55.00	10.00
Cat 7	G (Thumb latch)	50.00	30	35.00	10.00
Cat 2	G (Thumb latch)	54.00	141	110.00	20.00
Dog 2	BB1 (O at back, high) . .	48.00	30	80.00	60.00
Dog 3	BB1 (O at back, high) . .	20.00	85	55.00	10.00
Dog 2	M (Lever outside)	15.00	95	140.00	30.00
Dog 1	FF[1]	30.00	110	135.00	60.00
Chick 89	X (see page 53)	20.00	30	60.00	30.00
Cat 13	KKK,[2][3]	40.00	65	60.00	10.00

animals failed because they did not *attend* to the process of being put through the movement, that, had they attended to it, they would later themselves have made the movement. It is, however, improbable that out of fifty times an animal should not have attended to what was going on at least two or three times. But if seeing himself do it was on a par with feeling an impulse to and so doing it, even two or three times would suffice to start the habit. And it is even more improbable that an experience should be followed by keen pleasure fifty times and not be attended to with might and

[1] FF was a box 40 × 21 × 24 inches, the door of which could be opened by putting the paw out between the bars to its right and pulling a loop which hung 16 inches above the floor, 4 inches out from the box and 6 inches to the right of the door.

[2] KKK was box K with both bolts removed. All that had to be done was to poke the paw out at one side of the door and press down a little bar of wood.

[3] The cats and chick were left in for two minutes at each trial, the dogs for from one to one and a half minutes.

main, unless animals attend *only* to their own impulses and the excitements thereof. But if the latter be true, it simply affirms our view from a more fundamental standpoint.

In another set of experiments animals were put in boxes with whose mechanisms they had had no experience, and from which they might or might not be able to escape by their own impulsive acts. The object was to see whether the time taken to form the association could be altered by my instruction. The results turned out to give a better proof of the inability to form an association by being put through the act than any failure to change the time-curve. For it happened in all but one of the cases that the movement which the animal made to open the door was different from the movement which I had put him through. Thus, several cats were put through (in Box C [button]) the following movement: I took the right paw and, putting it against the lower right-hand side of the button, pushed it round to a horizontal position. The cats' ways were as follows: No. 1 turned it by clawing vigorously at its top; No. 6, by pushing it round with his nose; No. 7, in the course of an indiscriminate scramble at first, in later trials either by pushing with his nose or clawing at the top, settling down finally to the last method. Nos. 2 and 5 did it as No. 1 did. Cat 2 was tried in B (O at back). I took his paw and pressed the loop with it, but he formed the habit of clawing and biting the string at the top of the box near the front. No. 1 was tried in A. I pressed the loop with his paw, but he formed the habit of biting at it.

In every case I kept on putting the animal through the act every time, if at the end of two minutes (one in several cases) it had not done it, even after it had shown, by using a different way, that my instruction had no influence. I never succeeded in getting the animal to change its way for mine. Moreover, if any one should fancy that the animal really profited by my instruction so as to learn what result to attain, namely, the turning of a certain button, but chose a way of his own to turn it, he would be deluding himself. The time taken to learn the act with instruction was no shorter than without.

If, then, an animal happens to learn an act by being put through it, it is just happening, nothing more. Of course, you may *direct* the animal's efforts so that he will perform the act himself the sooner. For instance, you may hold him so that his accidental pawing will be sure to hit the vital point of the contrivance. But the animal cannot form an association leading to an act unless the particular impulse to that act is present as an element of the association; he cannot supply it from a general stock. The groundwork of animal associations is not the association of *ideas*, but the association of idea or sense-impression with *impulse*.

In the questionnaire mentioned elsewhere, some questions were asked with a view to obtaining corroboration or refutation of this theory that an impulse or innervation is a necessary element in every association formed if that association leads to an act. The questions and answers were :—

Question 1: "If you wanted to teach a horse to tap seven times with his hoof when you asked him, 'How many days are there in a week ?,' would you teach him by taking his leg and making him go through the motions?"

A answered, "Yes ! at first."

B answered, "No ! I would not."

C answered, "At first, yes !"

D answered, "No !"

Question 2: "Do you think you *could* teach him that way, even if naturally you would take some other way?"

A answered, "In time, yes !"

B answered, "I think it would be a very hard way."

C answered, "Certainly I do."

D answered, "I do not think I could."

E answered, "Yes."

Question 3: "How would you teach him?"

A answered, "I should tap his foot with a whip, so that he would raise it, and reward him each time."

B answered, "I should teach him by the motion of the whip."

C answered, "First teach him by pricking his leg the number of times you wanted his foot lifted."

D answered, "You put figure 2 on blackboard and touch him on leg twice with cane, and so on."

E answered ambiguously.

It is noteworthy that even those who think they *could* teach an animal by putting him through the trick do not use that method, except at first. And what they really do then is probably to stimulate the animal to the reflex act of raising his hoof. The hand simply replaces the cane or whip as the means of stimulus. The answers are especially instructive, because the numerous counting tricks done by trained horses seem, at first, to be incomprehensible, unless the trainer can teach the horse by putting it through the movement the proper number of times. The counting tricks performed by Mascot, Professor Maguire's horse, were quoted to me by a friend as incomprehensible on my theory. The answers given above show how simple the thing really is. All the counting-tricks of all the intelligent horses depend on the fact that a horse raises his hoof when a certain stimulus is given. One simple reaction gives the basis for a multitude of tricks. In the same way other tricks, which at first sight seem to require that the animal should learn by being put through the movement, may depend on some simple reflex or natural impulse.

Another question was, "How would you teach a cat to get out of a box, the door of which was closed with a thumb latch?"

A answered, "I should use a puffball as a plaything for the cat to claw at." This means, I suppose, that he would get the cat to claw at the puffball and thus direct its clawings to the vicinity of the thumb piece.

B answered, "I would put the cat in and get it good and hungry and then open the door by lifting the latch with my finger. Then put some food that the cat likes outside, and she will soon try to imitate you and so learn the trick."

C answered, "I would first adjust all things in connection with the surroundings of the cat so they would be applicable to the laws of its nature, and then proceed to teach the trick."

I suppose this last means that he would fix the box so that some of the cat's instinctive acts would lead it to perform the trick. The answer given by *B* means apparently that he would simply leave the thing to accident, for any such imitation as he supposes is out of the question. At all events, none of these would naturally start to teach the trick by putting the animal through the motions, which, were it a possible way, would probably be a traditional one among trainers. On the whole, I see in these data no reason for modifying our dogma that animals cannot learn acts without the impulse.

Presumably the reader has already seen budding out of this dogma a new possibility, a further simplification of our theories about animal consciousness. The possibility is that animals may have *no images or memories at all, no ideas to associate.* Perhaps the entire fact of association in animals is the presence of sense-impressions with which are associated, by resultant pleasure, certain impulses, and that, therefore, and therefore only, a certain situation brings forth a certain act. Returning to our analysis of the association, this theory would say that there was no (9) or (10) or (3) or (4), that the sense-impression gave rise, when accompanied by the feeling of discomfort, to the impulse (5) directly, without the intervention of any representations of the taste of the food, or the experience of being outside, or the sight of oneself doing the act. This theory might be modified so as to allow that the representations could be there, but to deny that they were necessary, were inevitably present, that the impulse was connected to the sense-impression through them. It would then claim that the effective part of the association was a direct bond between the situation and the impulse, but would not cut off the possiblity of there being an aura of memories along with the process. It then becomes a minor question of interpretation which will doubtless sooner or later demand an answer. I shall not try to answer it now. The more radical question, the question of the utter exclusion of representative trains of thought, of any genuine association of *ideas* from the mental life of animals, is worth serious consideration. I confess that, although certain authentic anecdotes and certain experiments, to be described soon, lead me to reject this exclusion, there are many qualities in animals' behavior which seem to back it up. If one takes his stand by a rigid application of the law of parsimony, he will find justification for this view which no experiments of mine can overthrow.

Of one thing I am sure, and that is that it is worth while to state the question and how to solve it, for although the point of view involved is far removed from that of our leading psychologists to-day, it cannot long remain so. I am sorry that I cannot pretend to give a final decision.

The view seems preposterous because, if an animal has sense-impressions when his brain is excited by currents starting in the end-organs, it seems incredible that he should not be conscious in imagination and memory by having similar excitations caused from within. We are accustomed to think of memory as the companion of sensation. But, after all, it is a question of fact whether the connections in the cat brain include connections between present sensation-neuroses and past sensation-neuroses. The only connections may be those between the former and impulse-neuroses, and there is no authoritative reason why we should suppose any others unless they are demonstrated by the cat's behavior. This is just the point at issue. Such evidence as the phenomena of animals' dreams does not at all prove the presence of memory or imagination. A dog may very well growl in his sleep without any idea of a hostile dog. The impulse to growl *may* be caused by chance excitement of its own neurosis without any sensation-neurosis being concerned. *Acts* of recognition may have no *feelings* of recognition going with or causing them. A sense-impression of me gets associated in my dog's mind with the impulses to jump on me, lick my hand, wag his tail, etc. If, after a year, the connection between the two has lasted, he will surely jump on me, lick my hand and wag his tail, though he has not and never had any representation of me.

The only logical way to go at this question and settle it is, I think, to find some associations the formation of which requires the presence of images, of ideas. You have to give an animal a chance to associate sense-impression A with sense-impression B and then to associate B with some act C so that the presence of B in the mind will lead to the performance of C. Presumably the representation of B, if present, will lead to C just as the sense-impression B did. Now, if the chance to associate B with A has been improved, you ought, when the animal is confronted with the sense-impression A, to get a revival of B and so the act C. Such a result would, if all chance to associate C with A had been eliminated, demonstrate the presence of representations and their associations. I performed such an experiment in a form modified so as to make it practicable with my animals and resources. Unfortunately, this modification spoils the crucial nature of the experiment and robs it of much of its authority. The experiment was as follows:—

A cat was in the big box where they were kept (see p. 90) very hungry. As I had been for a long time the source of all food, the cats had grown to watch me very carefully. I sat, during the experiment, about eight feet from the box, and would at intervals of two minutes clap my hands four times and say, "I must feed those cats." Of course the cat would at first feel no impulse except perhaps to watch me more closely when this signal was given. After ten seconds had elapsed I would take a piece of fish, go up to the cage and hold it through the wire netting, three feet from the floor. The cat would then, of course, feel the impulse to climb up the front of the cage. In fact, experience had previously established the habit of climbing up whenever I moved toward the cage, so that in the experiment the cat did not ordinarily wait until I arrived there with the fish. In this experiment

A = The sense-impression of my movements and voice when giving the signal.

B = The sense-impression of my movements in taking fish, rising, walking to box, etc.

C = The act of climbing up, with the impulse leading thereunto.

The question was whether after a while A would remind the cat of B, and cause him to do C before he got the *sense-impression* of B, that is, before the ten seconds were up.   If A leads to C through a memory of B, animals surely *can* have association of ideas proper, and probably often *do*. Now, as a fact, after from thirty to sixty trials, the cat does perform C immediately on being confronted by A or some seconds later, at all events before B is presented.   And it is my present opinion that their action is to be explained by the presence, through association, of the idea B.   But it is not impossible that A was associated *directly* with the impulse to C, although that impulse was removed from it by ten seconds of time.   Such an association is, it seems to me, highly improbable, unless the neurosis of A, and with it the psychosis, continues until the impulse to C appears.   But if it does so continue during the ten seconds, and thus get directly linked to C, we have exactly a representation, an image, a memory, in the mind for eight of those ten seconds. It does not help the deniers of images to substitute an image of A for an image of B.   Yet, unless they do this, they have to suppose that A comes and goes, and that after ten seconds C comes, and, passing over the intervening blank, willfully chooses out A and associates itself with it.   There are some other considerations regarding the behavior of the cats from the time the signal was given till they climbed up, which may be omitted in the hope that it will soon be possible to perform a decisive experiment.   If an observer can make sure of the animal's attention to a sequence A–B, where B does not arouse any impulse to an act, and then later get the animal to associate B with C, leaving A out this time, he may then, if A, when presented anew, arouses C, bid the deniers of representations to forever hold their peace.

Another reason for allowing animals representations and images is found in the longer time taken to form the association between the act of licking or scratching and the consequent escape. If the associations in general were simply between situation and impulse and act, one would suppose that the situation would be associated with the impulse to lick or scratch as readily as with the impulse to turn a button or claw a string. Such is not the case. By comparing the curves for Z on pages 57–58 with the others, one sees that for so simple an act it takes a long time to form the association. This is not a final reason, for lack of attention, a slight increase in the time taken to open the door after the act was done, or an absence of preparation in the nervous system for connections between these particular acts and definite sense-impressions, may very well have been the cause of the difficulty in forming the associations. Nor is it certain that *ideas* of clawing loops would be easier to form than ideas of scratching or licking oneself. The matter is still open to question. But, as said before, my opinion would be that animals *do* have representations and that such are the beginning of the rich life of ideas in man. For the most part, however, such are confined to specific and narrow practical lines. There was no evidence that my animals habitually *did* form associations of ideas from their experience throughout, or that such were constantly revived without the spur of immediate practical advantage.[1]

[1] One result of the application of experimental method to the study of the intellect of animals was the distinction of learning by the selection of impulses or acts from learning by the selection of ideas. The usual method of learning in the case of animals other than man was shown by the studies reprinted in this volume to be the direct selection, in a certain situation, of a desirable response and its association with that situation, not the indirect selection of such a response by the selection of some *idea* which then of itself produced the response. The animals did not usually behave as if they *thought of* getting freedom or food in a certain way and were thereby moved

Before leaving the topic an account may be given of experiments similar to the one described above as performed
on Cats 3 and 4, which were undertaken with Cat 13 and
Dogs 1, 2 and 3.

Cat 13 was fed with pieces of fish at the top of the wire
netting 45 times, to accustom it to climbing up when it saw

to do so, but as if the stimulus in question made immediate connection with
the response itself or an intimately associated impulse.

The experiments had in this respect both a negative or destructive and a
positive or constructive meaning. On the one hand, they showed that animal
learning was not homologous with human association of ideas, that animal
learning was not human learning *minus* abstract and conceptual thought,
but was on a still 'lower' level. On the other hand, the first positive evidence that animals could, under certain circumstances, learn, as man so
commonly does, by the indirect connection of a response with a situation
through some non-sensory relic or representative of the latter, came from my
experiments.

It was perhaps natural that the more exciting denial of habitual learning
by ideas should have attracted more attention than the somewhat tedious
experiments to prove that under certain conditions they could so learn.
At all events, a perverse tradition seems to have grown up to the effect that
I denied the possibility of animals having images or learning in any case by
representative thinking.

There is some excuse for this tradition in the fact that whereas the proof
that the habitual learning of these dogs and cats did not require 'ideas'
is clear and emphatic, my evidence that certain features of their behavior
did require 'ideas' is complicated and imperfect.

The fact seems to be that a 'free idea' comes in the animals or in man
only as a result of a somewhat elaborate process of analysis or extraction from
a gross total sensory process. The primary level or grade of experience,
common to animals and little babies, comprises states of mind such as an
adult man gets if lost in anger, fear, suffocation, dyspepsia, looking at a
panorama of unknown objects with head upside down, smelling the mixture
of odors of a soap factory, driving a golf ball, dashing to the net in a game of
tennis, warding off a blow, or swimming under water. For a man to get a
distinct controllable percept of approaching asthma, of a carpet loom seen
upside down, or of a successful 'carry through,' or 'smash' or 'lob,'
so that one knows just what one is experiencing or doing, and can recall
just what one experienced or did, requires further experience of the element
in question — contemplation of it in isolation or dealings with it in many varied

me come with fish. I then went through the same process as with 3 and 4, but at intervals of 60 to 90 seconds instead of 120. After 90 such trials it occasionally climbed up a little way, but though 135 trials in all were given, it never made the uniform and definite reaction which 3 and 4 did. It reacted, when it reacted at all, at from 5 to 9 seconds after the signal. Whether age, weight, lack of previous habitual climbing when I approached, or a slowness in forming the association made the difference, is uncertain.

Dog 1 was experimented on in the following manner: I would put him in a big pen, 20–10 feet, and sit outside facing it, he watching me as was his habit. I would pound with a stick and say, "Go over to the corner." After an interval (10 seconds for 35 trials, 5 seconds for 60 trials) I would go over to the corner (12 feet off) and drop a piece of meat there. He, of course, followed and secured it. On the 6th,

connections. So for a cat to get a distinct controllable percept of a loop, or of its own clawing or nosing or pulling, it must have the capacity to analyze such elements out of the total gross complexes in which they inhere, and also certain means or stimuli to such analysis.

This capacity or tendency the cats and dogs do, in my opinion, possess, though in a far less degree than the average child. They also suffer from lack of stimuli to the exercise of the capacity. Their confinement, for the most part, to the direct sensory experience of things and acts, is due in part to the weakness of the capacity or tendency of their neurones to act in great detail, and in part to the lack of such stimuli as visual exploration of things in detail, manual manipulation of the same thing in many ways, and the identification of elements of objects and acts by language. They get few free ideas because they are less ready than man to get them under the same conditions and because their instinctive behavior and social environment offer conditions that are less favorable. The task of getting an animal to have some free ideational representative of a red loop or of pushing up a button with the nose may be compared with that of getting a very stupid boy to have a free ideational representative of acceleration, or of the act of sounding *th*. The difference between them and man which is so emphasized in the text, though real and of enormous practical importance, is thus not at all a mysterious gap or trackless desert. We can see our way from animal to human learning.

7th, 16th, 17th, 18th and 19th trials he did perform the act before the 10 seconds were up, then for several times went during the two-minute intervals without regarding the signal, and finally abandoned the habit altogether, although he showed by his behavior when the signal was given that he was not indifferent to it.

Dogs 1, 2 and 3 were also given 95, 135 and 95 trials, respectively, the acts done being (1) standing up against the wire netting inclosing the pen, (2) placing the paws on top of a keg, and (3) jumping up onto a box. The time intervals were 5 seconds in each case. No dog of these ever performed the act before I started to take the meat to feed them, but they did show, by getting up if they were lying down when the signal was given, or by coming to me if they were in some other part of the pen, that something was suggested to them by it. Why these cases differ from the cases of Cats 3 and 4 (10 and 12 also presented phenomena like those reported in the cases of 3 and 4) is an interesting though not very important question. The dogs were not kept so hungry as were the cats, and experience had certainly not rendered the particular impulses involved so sensitive, so ready to discharge. Dogs 2 and 3 were older. There is no reason to invoke any qualitative difference in the mental make-up of the animals until more illuminating experiments are made.

ASSOCIATION BY SIMILARITY AND THE FORMATION OF CONCEPTS

What there is to say on this subject from the standpoint of my experiments will be best introduced by an account of the experiments themselves.

Dog 1 had escaped from AA (O at front) 26 times. He

was then put in BB (O at back). Now, whereas 2 and 3, who
were put in without previous experience with AA, failed to
paw the loop in BB, No. 1 succeeded.   His times were 7.00,
.35, 2.05, .40, .32, .10, 1.10, .38, .10, .05, and from then on he
pawed the loop as soon as put in the box.   After a day or so
he was put in BB1 (O at back high).   Although the loop
was in a new position, his times were only .20, .10, .10, etc.
After nine days he was put in a box arranged with a little
wooden platform 2½ inches square, hung where the loop was
in BB1.   Although the platform resembled the loop not
the least save in position, his times were only .10, .07, .05,
etc.

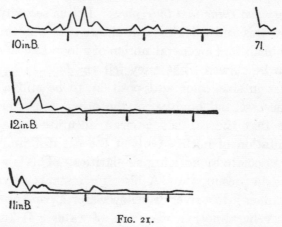

FIG. 21.

From the curves given in Figure 21, which tell the history
of 10, 11 and 12 in B1 (O at back) after each had previously
been familiarized with A (O at front), we see this same
influence of practice in reacting to one mechanism upon the
time taken to react to a mechanism at all similar.   It naturally takes a cat a longer time to accidentally claw a loop in
the back than in the front, yet a comparison of these curves
with those on page 39, Figure 2, shows the opposite to have
been the case with 10, 11 and 12.   The same remarkable

quickness was noted in Cats 1 and 3 when put into B (O at back) after learning A (O at front). Moreover, the loops were not alike. The loop in A was of smaller wire, covered with a bluish thread, while the loop in B was covered with a black rubber compound, the diameter of the loop being three times that of A's loop.

If any advocate of reason in animals has read so far, I doubt not that his heart has leaped with joy at these two preceding paragraphs. "How," he will say, "can you explain these facts without that prime factor in human reason, association by similarity? Surely they show the animal perceiving likenesses and acting from general ideas." *This is the very last thing that they show.* Let us see why they do not show this and what they do show. He who thinks that these animals had a general notion of a loop-like thing as the thing to be clawed, that they felt the loop in B, different as it was in size, color and position, to be still a loop, to have the essential quality of the other, must needs presuppose that the cat has a clear, accurate sensation and representation of both. Only if the cat discriminates can it later associate by noticing similarities. This is what such thinkers do presuppose. A bird, for instance, dives in the same manner into a river of yellow water, a pond or an ocean. It has a general notion, they say, of water. It knows that river water is one thing and pond water another thing, but it knows that both are water, *ergo*, fit to dive into. The cat who reacts to a loop of small wire of a blue color knows just what that loop is, and when it sees a different loop, knows its differences, but knows also its likeness, and reacts to the essential. Thus crediting the cat with our differentiation and perception of individuality, they credit it with our conceptions and perceptions of similarity. Unless the animal has the first, there is no reason to suppose the last.

Now, *the animal does not have either.* It does not in the first place react to that particular loop in A, with recognition of its qualities. It reacts to a vague, ill-defined sense-impression, undiscriminated and even unperceived in the technical sense of the word. Morgan's phrase, "a bit of pure experience," is perhaps as good as any. The loop is to the cat what the ocean is to a man, when thrown into it when half-asleep. Thus the cat who climbed up the front of the cage whenever I said, "I must feed those cats," would climb up just as inevitably when I said, "My name is Thorndike," or "To-day is Tuesday." So cats would claw at the loop or button when the door was open. So cats would paw at the place where a loop had been, though none was there. The reaction is not to a well-discriminated object, but to a vague situation, and any element of the situation may arouse the reaction. The whole situation in the case of man is speedily resolved into elements; the particular elements are held in focus, and the non-essential is systematically kept out of mind. In the animal the whole situation sets loose the impulse; all of its elements, including the non-essentials, get yoked with the impulse, and the situation may be added to or subtracted from without destroying the association, provided you leave something which will set off the impulse. The animal does not think one is like the other, nor does it, as is so often said, mistake one for the other. It does not think *about* it at all; it just thinks *it*, and the *it* is the kind of "pure experience " we have been describing. In human mental life we have accurate, discriminated sensations and perceptions, realized as such, and general notions, also realized as such. Now, what the phenomena in animals which we have been considering show is that they have neither. Far from showing an advanced stage of mentality, they show a very primitive and unspecialized stage.

They are to be explained not by the presence of *general* notions, but by the absence of notions of *particulars*. The idea that animals react to a particular and absolutely defined and realized sense-impression, and that a similar reaction to a sense-impression which varies from the first proves an association by similarity, is a myth. We shall see later how an animal does come in certain cases to discriminate, in one sense of the word, with a great degree of delicacy, but we shall also see then what must be emphasized now, that naturally the animal's brain reacts very coarsely to sense-impressions, and that the animal does not think *about* his thoughts at all.

This puts a new face upon the question of the origin and development of human abstractions and consequent general ideas. It has been commonly supposed that animals had 'recepts' or such semi-abstractions as Morgan's 'predominants,' and that by associating with these, arbitrary and permanent signs, such as articulate sounds, one turned them into genuine ideas of qualities. Professor James has made the simple but brilliant criticism that all a recept really means is *a tendency to react in a certain way*. But I have tried to show that the fact that an animal reacts alike to a lot of things gives no reason to believe that it is conscious of their common quality and reacts to that consciousness, because the things it reacts to in the first place are not the hard-and-fast, well-defined 'things'[1] of human life. What a 'recept' or 'predominan ' really stands for is no thing which can be transformed into a notion of a quality by being labelled with a name. This easy solution of the problem of abstraction is impossible. A true idea of the problem itself is better than such a solution.

My statement of what has been the course of development along this line is derived from observations of animals' behavior and Professor James' theory of the nature of and presumable brain processes going with the abstractions and conceptions of human consciousness, but it is justified chiefly by its harmony with the view that conception, the faculty of having general notions, has been naturally selected by reason of its utility. The first thing is for an animal to learn to react alike only to things which resemble each other in the *essential* qualities. On an artificial, analytic basis, feelings of abstract qualities might grow out of reacting alike to objects similar in such a respect that the reaction would be useless or harmful. But in the actual struggle for existence, starting with the mammalian mind as we have found it, you will tend to get reactions to the *beneficial* similarities by selection from among these so-called mistakes, *before you get any general faculty of noticing similarities*. In order that this faculty of indifferent reaction to different things shall grow into the useful faculty of indifferent reaction to different things *which have all some quality that makes the reaction a fit one*, there must be a tremendous range of associations. For a lot of the similarities which are non-essential have to be stamped out, not by a power of feeling likeness, but by their failure to lead to pleasure. With such a wide range of associations we may get reactions on the one hand where impulses have been connected with one particular sense-impression because when connected with all others they had failed to give pleasure, and on the other hand, reactions where an impulse has been connected with numerous different impressions possessing one common quality, and disconnected with all impressions, otherwise like these, which fail to have that one quality.

Combined with this multiplication of associations, there is, I think, an equally important factor, the loosening of the elements of an association from one another and from it as a

whole.   Probably the idea of the look of the loop or lever or
thumb latch never entered the mind of any one of my cats
during the months that they were with me, except when the
front end of the association containing it was excited by putting the cat into the box.   In general, the unit of their consciousness, apart from impulses and emotions, is a whole
association-series.   Such soil cannot grow general ideas, for
the ideas, so long as they never show themselves except for
a particular practical business, will not be thought about or
realized in their nature or connections.   If enough associations are provided by a general curiosity, such as is seen
among the monkeys, if the mental elements of the association are freed, isolated, felt by themselves, *then* a realization
of the ideas, feelings of their similarity by transition from
one to the other, feelings of qualities and of meanings, may
gradually emerge.   Language will be a factor in the isolation of the ideas and a help to their realization.   But when
any one says that language has been the cause of the change
from brute to man, when one talks as if *nothing but it* were
needed to turn animal consciousness into human, he is speaking as foolishly as one who should say that a proboscis added
to a cow would make it an elephant.

   This is all I have to say, in this connection, about association by similarity and conception, and with it is concluded
our analysis of the nature of the association-process in animals.   Before proceeding to treat of the delicacy, complexity, number and permanence of these associations, it
seems worth while to attempt to describe graphically, not by
analysis, the mental fact we have been studying, and also
to connect our results with the previous theories of association.

   One who has seen the phenomena so far described, who
has watched the life of a cat or dog for a month or more

under test conditions, gets, or fancies he gets, a fairly definite idea of what the intellectual life of a cat or dog feels like. It is most like what we feel when consciousness contains little thought about anything, when we feel the sense-impressions in their first intention, so to speak, when we feel our own body, and the impulses we give to it. Sometimes one gets this animal consciousness while in swimming, for example. One feels the water, the sky, the birds above, but with no thoughts *about* them or memories of how they looked at other times, or æsthetic judgments about their beauty; one feels no *ideas* about what movements he will make, but feels himself make them, feels his body throughout. Self-consciousness dies away. Social consciousness dies away. The meanings, and values, and connections of things die away. One feels sense-impressions, has impulses, feels the movements he makes; that is all.

This pictorial description may be supplemented by an account of some associations in human life which are learned in the same way as are animal associations; associations, therefore, where the process of formation is possibly homologous with that in animals. When a man learns to swim, to play tennis or billiards, or to juggle, the process is something like what happens when the cat learns to pull the string to get out of the box, provided, of course, we remove, in the man's case, all the accompanying mentality which is not directly concerned in learning the feat.[1] Like the latter, the former

---

[1] A man may learn to swim from the general feeling, "I want to be able to swim." While learning, he may think of this desire, of the difficulties of the motion, of the instruction given him, or of anything which may turn up in his mind. This is all extraneous and is not concerned in the acquisition of the association. Nothing like it, of course, goes on in the animal's mind. Imagine a man thrown into the water repeatedly, and gradually floundering to the shore in better and better style until finally, when thrown in, he swims off perfectly, and deprive the man of all extraneous feelings, and you have

contains desire, sense-impression, impulse, act and possible representations. Like it, the former is learned gradually. Moreover, the associations concerned cannot be formed by imitation. One does not know how to dive just by seeing another man dive. You cannot form them from being put through them, though, of course, this helps indirectly, in a way that it does not with animals. One makes use of no feelings of a common element, no perceptions of similarity. The tennis player does not feel, "This ball coming at this angle and with this speed is similar in angle, though not in speed, to that other ball of an hour ago, therefore I will hit it in a similar way." He simply feels an impulse from the sense-impression. Finally, the elements of the associations are not isolated. No tennis player's stream of thought is filled with free-floating representations of any of the tens of thousands of sense-impressions or movements he has seen and made on the tennis court. Yet there is consciousness enough at the time, keen consciousness of the sense-impressions, impulses, feelings of one's bodily acts. So with the animals. There is consciousness enough, but of this kind.

Thus, the associations in human life, which compare with the simple connections learned by animals, are associations involving connections between novel, complex and often inconstant sense-impressions and impulses to acts similarly novel, complex and often inconstant. Man has the elements of most of his associations in isolated form, attended to separately, possessed as a permanent fund, recallable at will, and multifariously connected among themselves, but

an approximate homologue of the process in animals. He feels discomfort, certain impulses to flounder around, some of which are the right ones to move his body to the shore. The pleasure which follows stamps in these, and gradually the proper movements are made immediately on feeling the sense-impression of surrounding water.

with these associations which we have mentioned, and with others like them, he deals as the animals deal with theirs. The process, in the man's mind, leaving out extraneous mental stuff, may be homologous to the association-process in animals. Of course, by assiduous attention to the elements of these associations, a man may isolate them, may thus get these associations to the same plane as the rest. But they pass through the stage we have described, even then, and with most men, stay there. The abstraction, the naming, etc., generally come from observers of the game or action, and concern things as felt by them, not by the participant.

CRITICISM OF PREVIOUS THEORIES

We may now look for a moment at what previous writers have said about the nature of association in animals. The complaint was made early in this book that all the statements had been exceedingly vague and of no value, except as retorts to the ' reason ' school. In the course of the discussion I have tried to extricate from this vagueness definite statements about imitation, association of ideas, association by ideas. There is one more theory, more or less hidden in the vagueness, — the theory that association in animals is the same as association in man, that the animal mind differs from the human mind only by the absence of reason and what it implies. Presumably, silence about what association is, means that it is the association which human psychology discusses. When the silence is broken, we get such utterances of this theory as the following : —

"I think we may say then that the higher animals are able to proceed a long way in the formation and definition of highly complex constructs, analogous to but probably differing somewhat from those which we form ourselves. These constructs, moreover, through association with reconstructs, or representations, link themselves in trains so that a sensation, or group of sensations, may suggest a series of reconstructs, or a series of remembered phenomena." (C. L. Morgan, Animal Life and Intelligence, p. 341.)

"Lastly, before taking leave of the subject of the chapter, I am most anxious that it should not be thought that, in contending that intelligence is not reason, I wish in any way to disparage intelligence. Nine tenths at least of the actions of average men are intelligent and not rational. Do we not all of us know hundreds of practical men who are in the highest degree intelligent, but in whom the rational, analytic faculty is but little developed? Is it any injustice to the brutes to contend that their inferences are of the same order as those of these excellent practical folk? In any case, no such injustice is intended; and if I deny them self-consciousness and reason, I grant to the higher animals perceptions of marvelous acuteness and intelligent inferences of wonderful accuracy and precision — intelligent inferences in some cases, no doubt, more perfect even than those of man, who is often disturbed by many thoughts " (*ibid.*, pp. 376–377).

"Language and the analytic faculty it renders possible differentiate man from the brute" (*ibid.*, p. 376).

Here, as elsewhere, it should be remembered that Lloyd Morgan is not quoted because he is the worst offender or because he represents the opposite in general of what the present writer takes to be the truth. On the contrary, Morgan is quoted because he is the least offender, because he has taken the most advanced stand along the line of the present investigation, because my differences from him are in the line of his differences from other writers. With the theory of the passages just quoted, however, which attribute extensive association of ideas and general powers comparable to those of men minus reason, to the brutes, and which repeat the time-honored distinction by language, I do not, in the least, agree. Association in animals does not equal association in man. The latter is built over and permeated and transformed by inference and judgment and comparison; it includes imitation in our narrow sense of transferred association; it obtains where no impulse is included; it thus takes frequently the form of long trains of thought ending in no pleasure-giving act; its elements are often loose, existing independently of the particular association; the association is not only thought, but at the same time thought *about*. None of these statements may be truthfully made of animal association. Only a small part of human association is at all comparable to it. My opinion of what that small part is has already been given. Moreover, further differences will be found as we consider the data relating to the delicacy, complexity, number, and permanence of associations in animals. I said a while ago that man was no more an animal with language than an elephant was a cow with a proboscis. We may safely broaden the statement and say that *man is not an animal plus reason*. It has been one great purpose of this investigation to show that even after leaving reason out of account, there are tremendous differences between man and the higher animals. The problem of comparative psychology is not only to get human reason from some lower faculties, but to get human *association* from animal association.

Our analysis, necessarily imperfect because the first attempted, of the nature of the association-process in animals is finished, and we have now to speak of its limitations in respect to delicacy, complexity, number and permanence.

DELICACY OF ASSOCIATIONS

It goes without saying that the possible delicacy of associations is conditioned by the delicacy of sense-powers. If an animal doesn't feel differently at seeing two objects, it cannot associate one with one reaction, the other with another. An equally obvious factor is attention; what is not attended to will not be associated. Beyond this there is no *a priori* reason why an animal should not react differently to things varying only by the most delicate difference, and I am inclined to think an animal could; that any two objects with a difference appreciable by sensation which are also able to win attention may be reacted to differently. Experiments to show this are very tedious, and the practical question is, "What will the animal naturally attend to?" The difficulty, as all trainers say, is to get the animal's attention to your signal somehow. Then he will in time surely react differently, if you give him the chance, to a figure 7 on the blackboard from the way he does to a figure 8, to your question, "How many days are there in a week?" and to your question, "How many legs have you?" The chimpanzee in London that handed out 3, 4, 5, 6, or 7 straws at command was not thereby proved of remarkable intelligence or of remarkably delicate associative power. Any reputable animal trainer would be ashamed to exhibit a horse who could not do as much ' counting ' as that. The maximum of delicacy in associating exhibited by any animal, to my knowledge, is displayed in the performance of the dog 'Dodgerfield,' exhibited by a Mr. Davis, who brings from four cards, numbered 1, 2, 3 and 4, whichever one his master shall *think of*. That is, you write out an arbitrary list, *e.g.* 4, 2, 1, 3, 3, 2, 2, 1, 4, 2, etc., and hand it to Mr. Davis, who looks at the list, thinks of the first number, says "Attention!

Dodger !" and then, "Bring it." This the dog does and so on through the list. Mr. Davis makes no signals which anyone sitting even right beside or in front of him can detect. Thus the dog exceeds the human observers in delicacy and associates each with a separate act four attitudes of his master, which to human observers seem all alike. Mr. Davis says he thinks the dog is a mind reader. I think it quite possible that whatever signs the dog goes by are given unconsciously and consist only of some very delicate general differences in facial expression or the manner of saying the words, "Bring it," or slight sounds made by Mr. Davis in thinking to himself the words one or two or three or four. Mr. Davis keeps his eyes shut and his hands behind a newspaper. The dog looks directly at his face.

To such a height possible delicacy may attain, but possible delicacy is quite another thing from actual untrained and unstimulated delicacy. The difference in reaction has to be brought about by associating with pleasure the reaction to the different sense-impression when it itself differs and associating with pain tendencies to confuse the reactions. The animal does not naturally as a function of sense-powers discriminate at all delicately. Thus the cat who climbed up the wire netting when I said, "I must feed those cats !" did not have a delicate association of just that act with just those words. For after I had dropped the clapping part of the signal and simply used those words, it would react just as vigorously to the words, "To-morrow is Tuesday" or "My name is Thorndike." The reaction naturally was to a very vague stimulus. Taking cat 10 when just beginning to learn to climb up at the signal, "I must feed those cats !" I started in to improve the delicacy, by opposing to this formula the formula, "I will not feed them," after saying which, I kept my word. That is, I gave sometimes the former signal and fed the cats, sometimes the latter and did not. The object was to see how long the cat would be in learning always to go up when I gave the first, never to do so when I gave the second signal. I said the words in both cases as I naturally would do, so that there was a difference in emphasis and tone as well as in the mere nature of the syllables. The two signals were given in all sorts of combinations so that there was no regularity in the recurrence of either which might aid the animal. The cat at first did not always climb up at the first signal and often *did* climb up at the wrong one. The change from this condition to one of perfect discrimination is shown in the accompanying curves (Fig. 22), one show-

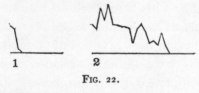

FIG. 22.

ing the decrease in *failures* to respond to the wrong signal. The first curve is formed by a line joining the tops of perpendiculars erected at intervals of 1 mm. along the abscissa. The height of a perpendicular represents the number of times the cat failed to respond to the food-signal in 20 trials, a height of 1 mm. being the representative of one failure. Thus, the entire curve stands for 280 trials, there being no failures after 60 trials, and only 1 after the 40th.

In the other curve, also, each 1 mm. along the abscissa stands for 20 trials, and the perpendiculars whose tops the curve unites represent the number of times the cat in each 20 *did* climb up at the signal which meant no food. It will be seen that 380 experiences were necessary before the animal learned that the second signal was different from the first. The experiment shows beautifully the animal method of acquisition. If at any stage the animal could have isolated the two ideas of the two sense-impressions, and felt them together in comparison, this long and tedious process would have been unnecessary.

It might be stated here that the animals also acquired associations of moderate delicacy in discriminating between the different boxes. No cat tried to get out of A or B by licking herself, for instance.

The question may naturally be raised that if naturally associations are thus vague, the common phenomenon of a dog obeying his master's commands, and no one else's, is inexplicable. The difference between one man and another, one voice and another, it may be said, is not much of a difference, yet is here uniformly discriminated, although we cannot suppose any such systematic training to reject the other slightly differing commands. My cats did not so discriminate. If any one else sat in my chair and called out, "I must feed the cats," they reacted, and probably very many animals would, if untroubled by emotions of curiosity or fear at the new individual, go through their tricks as well at another's voice as at that of their master. The other cases exemplify the influence of attention. Repeated attention to these sense-impressions has rendered them clear-cut and detailed, and the new impression consequently does not equal them in calling forth the reaction.

The main thing to carry away from this discussion is the assurance that the delicacy of the animal in associating acts with impressions is nothing like the delicacy of the man who feels that a certain tone is higher, or weight is heavier, than another, but *is* like the delicacy of the man who runs to a certain spot to hit one tennis ball and to a different spot to hit one coming with a slightly different speed.

COMPLEXITY OF ASSOCIATIONS

An important question, especially if one wishes to rate an animal on a scale of intelligence, is the question of how complex an association it can form. A man can learn that to open a door he has to put the key in its hole, turn it, turn the knob, and pull the door. Here, then, is a complex act connected with the simple sense-impression. Or, conversely, a man knows that when the ringing of a bell is followed by a whistle and that by a red light he is to do a certain thing, while if any of the three happens alone, he is not to. How far, then, we ask, can animals go along the line of increased complexity in the associations?

We must not mistake for a complex association a series of associations, where one sense-impression leads to an act such as to present a new sense-impression which leads to another act which in its turn leads to a new sense-impression. Of the formation of such *series* animals are capable to a very high degree. Chicks from 10 to 25 days old learned to go directly through a sort of big labyrinth requiring a series of 23 distinct and in some cases fairly difficult associations, of which 11 involved choices between two paths. By this power of acquiring a long series animals find their way to distant feeding grounds and back again. But all such cases are examples of the *number*, not of the complexity, of animal associations.

Some of my boxes were such as did give a chance for a complex association to be formed. Such were G (thumb latch), J (double), K and L (triples) for the cats, and O (triple) for the dogs. It would be possible for a cat, after stepping on the platform in K, to notice that the platform was in a different position, and so feel then a different sense-impression from before, and thus turn the thing into a serial association. The cat would then be like a man who on seeing a door should feel only the impulse to stick the key in the hole, but then, seeing the door plus a key in the hole, should feel the impulse to turn the key and so on through. My cats did not give any signs of this, so that with them it was either a complex association or an irregular happening of the proper impulses. Probably the same was the case with Dog 1. Cats 10, 11, 12 in L knew all the movements separately before being experimented on with the combination. Cats 2, 3, 4 had had some experience of D, which worked by a string something like the string part of K. The string in K was, however, quite differently situated and required an altogether different movement to pull it. Since further No. 2, who had had ten times as much experience in D as 3 or 4, succeeded no better with the string element of K than they, it is probable that the experience did not help very much. All else in all these compound associations was new. At the same time the history of these animals' dealings with these boxes would not fairly represent that of animals without general experience of clawing at all sorts of loose or shaky things in the inside of a box. These cats had learned to claw at all sorts of things. The time-curves were taken as in the formation of the other associations, and, in addition, the order in which the animal did the several things required was recorded in every trial.

In the case of all the curves, except the latter part of 3 in G, one notices a very gradual slope and an excessive irregularity in the curve throughout. Within the limits of the trials given the animals are unable to form a perfect association and what advancement they make is very slow. The case of 3 in G is not an exception to this, but a proof of it. For 3 succeeded in making a perfect association, by accidentally hitting on a way to turn the compound association into a simple one. He happened one time to paw down the thumb piece at the same time that his other fore limb, with which he was holding on between the door and the top of the box, was pressing against the door. This giving him success he repeated it in later trials and in a short time had it fixed as an element in a perfect association. The marked change in his curve, from an irregular and gradual slope at such a height as displayed a very imperfect association, to a constant and very slight height, shows precisely the change from a compound to a simple association.

Compound associations are formed slowly and not at all well. Further observation shows that they were really not formed at all. For the animals did not, except 3 in K for a certain period, do the several things in a constant order, nor did they do them only once apiece. On the contrary, an animal would pull the string several times after the bolt had gone up with its customary click, and would do sometimes one thing first, sometimes another. It may also be noted here, in advance of its proper place, that these compound associations are far below the simple in point of permanence. The conduct of the animals is clearly not that of minds having associated with a certain box's interior the idea of a succession of three movements. The animal does not feel, "I did this and that and that and got out," or, more simply still, "this and that and that means getting out." If it did, we should soon see it doing what was necessary without repetition and in a fairly constant time.

I imagine, however, that an animal could learn to associate with one sense-impression a compound act so as to perform its elements in a regular order. By arranging the box so that the second and third elements of the act could be performed *only after the first had been,* and the third *only after the first and second,* I am inclined to think you could get a very vigorous cat to learn the elements in order and form the association perfectly. The case is comparable to that of delicacy. The cat does not *tend* to know what he is doing or to depart from the hit-or-miss method of learning, but by associating the other combinations of elements with failure to get pleasure, as in delicacy experiments we associated the reactions to all but the one signal, you could probably stamp out all but the 1, 2, 3 order.

The fact that you have to thus maneuver to get the animals to have the three impulses in a regular order shows that even when they are so, there is no idea of the three as in an order, no thinking about them. Representations do not get beyond their first intention. They are not carried up into a free life which works them over anew. A complex *act* does not imply a complex *thought*, or, more exactly, a performance of a series does not imply the thought of a series. Consequently, since the complexity of the act depends on the power which failure has to stamp out all other combinations, it is far more limited than in man.

NUMBER OF ASSOCIATIONS

The patent and important fact is that there are so few in animals compared to the human stock. Even after taking into account the various acts associated with various smells, and exaggerating the possibility of getting an equipment of associations in this field which man lacks, one must recognize how far below man any animal is in respect to mere quantity of associations. The associations with words alone of an average American child of ten years far outnumber those of any dog. A good billiard player probably has more associations in connection with this single pastime than a dog with his whole life's business. In the associations which are homologous with those of animals man outdoes them and adds an infinity of associations of a different sort. The primates would seem, by virtue of their incessant curiosity and addition to experience not for any practical purpose but merely for love of mental life, to represent an advanced stage toward this tremendous quantity of associations. In man not only this activity and curiosity, but also education, increases the number of associations. Associations are formed more quickly, and the absence of need for self-support during a long infancy gives time. Associations thus formed work back upon practical life, and by showing better ways decrease the need of work, and so again increase the chance to form associations. The result in the case of a human mind to-day is the possession of a thesaurus of valuable associations, if the time has been wisely spent. The free life of ideas, imitation, all the methods of communication, and the original accomplishments which we may include under the head of invention, make the process of acquisition in many cases quite a different one from the trial and error method of the animals, and in general much shorten it.

Small as it is, however, the number of associations which an animal may acquire is probably much larger than popularly supposed.

My cats and dogs did not mix up their acts with the wrong sense-impressions. The chicks that learned the series of twenty-three associations did not find it a task beyond their powers to retain them. Several three-day-old chicks, which I caused to learn ten simple associations in the same day, kept the things apart and on the next morning went through each act at the proper stimulus. In the hands of animal trainers some animals get a large number of associations perfectly in hand.   The horse Mascot is claimed to know the meaning of fifteen hundred signals! He certainly knows a great many, and such as are naturally difficult of acquisition.   It would be an enlightening investigation if some one could find out just how many associations a cat or dog could form, if he were carefully and constantly given an opportunity.   The result would probably show that the number was limited only by the amount of motive available and the time taken to acquire each.   For there is probably nothing in their brain structure which limits the number of connections that can be formed, or would cause such connections, as they grew numerous, to become confused.

In their anxiety to credit animals with human powers, the psychologists have disregarded or belittled, perhaps, the possibilities of the strictly animal sort of association. They would think it more wonderful that a horse should respond differently to a lot of different numbers on the blackboard than that he should infer a consequence from premises.   But if it be made a direct question of pleasure or pain to an animal, he can associate any number of acts with different stimuli.   Only he does not form any associations until he has to, until the direct benefit is apparent, and, for his ordinary life, comparatively few are needed.

On the whole our judgment from a comparison of man's associations with the brutes' must be that a man's are naturally far more delicate, complex and numerous, and that in as far as the animals attain delicacy, complexity, or a great number of associations, they do it by methods which man uses only in a very limited part of the field.

Permanence of Associations

Once formed, the connections by which, when an animal feels a certain sense-impression, he does a certain thing, persist over considerable intervals of time. With the curves on pages 39 to 58 and 60 to 65 are given in many instances [1] additional curves showing the animal's proficiency after an interval without experience. To these data may be added the following: —

The three chicks that had learned to escape through the long labyrinth (involving twenty-three associations) succeeded in repeating the performance after ten days' interval. Similarly the chicks used as imitators in V, W, X and Y did not fail to perform the proper act after an interval of twenty days. Cat 6, who had had about a hundred experiences in C (button), had the association as perfect after twenty days as when it left off. Cat 2, who had had 36 experiences with C and had attained a constant time of 8 seconds, escaped fourteen days later in 3, 9 and 8 seconds, respectively, in three trials. Cat 1, after an interval of twenty days, failed in 10 minutes to escape from C. The signal for climbing up the front of the cage was reacted to by No. 3 after an interval of twenty-four days. No. 10, who had learned to discriminate between 'I must feed those cats' and 'I will not feed them,' was tried after *eighty days*. It was given 50 trials with the second signal mingled indiscriminately with 25 trials with the first. I give the full record of these, 'yes' equalling a trial in which she 'forgot' and climbed up, 'no' equalling a trial in which she wisely stayed down. Dashes represent intervening trials with the first

[1] See 10 in A, 3 in A, 10 in D; 10 in C, 4 in C, 3 in C; 6, 2, 5, 4 in E; 4 in F; 10 in H, 3 in H; 3, 4, 5, in I; 4 in G, 3 in G; 3 in K; 10 in L; dog 1 in N and CC; dog 1 in G and O.

signal, *to which she always reacted.* It will be observed
that 50 trials put the cat in the same position that 350 had
done in her first experience, although in that first experience
she had had only about a hundred trials after the association
had been perfected. The association between the first
signal and climbing up was perfect after the eighty days.

TABLE 8

TRIALS 1-7	TRIALS 8-17	TRIALS 18-27	TRIALS 28-35	TRIALS 36-42	TRIALS 43-50
——	yes	no	——	——	——
——	yes	yes	——	no	——
yes	yes	no	——	no	——
yes	——	no	no	——	——
no	yes	——	no	no	——
——	yes	——	yes	no	no
yes	no	yes	no	no	no
yes	yes	yes		——	yes
no	no	yes	no	——	no
no	——	yes	yes	no	no
——	——	no	no	no	no
——	yes	no	no		no
——	yes				no

All these data show that traces of the connections once
formed are very slow in being lost. If we allow that part
of the time in the first trial in all these cases is due to the
time taken to realize the situation (time not needed in the
trials when the association is forming and the animal is
constantly being dropped into boxes), we may say that the
association is as firm as ever for a considerable time after
practice at it is stopped. How long a time would be required to annul the influence of any given quantity of
experience, say of an association which had been gone
through with ten times, I cannot say. It could, if profitable,

easily be determined in any case.   The only case of total
loss of the association (No. 1 in C) is so exceptional that I
fancy something other than lapse of time was its cause.
The main interest of these data, considered as quantitative
estimates, is not psychological, but biological.   They show
what a tremendous advantage the well-developed association-process is to an animal.   The ways to different feeding
grounds, the actions of enemies, the appearance of noxious
foods, are all connected permanently with the proper reaction by a few experiences which need be reënforced only
very rarely.   Of course, associations without any permanence would be useless, but the usefulness increases im-
mensely with such a degree of permanence as these results
witness.   An interesting experiment from the biological
point of view would be to see how infrequently an experience
could occur and yet lead eventually to a perfect association.
An experiment approximating this is recorded in the time-
curves for Box H in Figure 7, on page 47.   Three trials at a
time were given, the trials being two or three days apart.
As may be seen from the curves, the association was readily
formed.

The chief psychological interest of these data is that they
show that permanence of associations *is not memory*.   The
fact that a cat, when after an interval she is put into box G,
proceeds to immediately press the thumb piece and push
the door, does not at all mean that the cat feels the box
to be the same from which she weeks ago freed herself by
pushing down that thumb piece, or thinks about ever
having felt or done anything in that box.   She does not
refer the present situation to a situation of the past and realize that it is the same, but simply feels on being confronted
with that situation the same impulse which she felt before.
She does the thing now for just the same reason that she

did it before, namely, because pleasure has connected that act above all others with that sense-impression, so that it is the one she feels like doing. Her condition is that of the swimmer who starts his summer season after a winter's deprivation. When he jumps off the pier and hits the water, he swims, not because he remembers that this is the way he dealt with water last summer and so applies his remembrance to present use, but just because experience has taught him to feel like swimming when he hits the water. All talk about recognition and memory in animals, if it asserts the presence of anything more than this, is a gross mistake. For real memory is an absolute thing, including everything but forgetfulness. If the cat had real memory, it would, when after an interval dropped into a box, remember that from this box it escaped by doing this or that and consequently, either immediately or after a time of recollection, go do it, or else it would not remember and would fail utterly to do it. On the contrary, we have all grades of *partial* 'forgetfulness,' just like the grades of swimming one might find if he dropped a dozen college professors into the mill ponds of their boyhood, just like the grades of forgetfulness of the associations once acquired on the ball field which are manifested when on the Fourth of July the 'solid men' of a town get out to amuse their fellow citizens. The animal makes attacks on a spot around the vital one, or claws at the thing — but not so precisely as before, or goes at it a while and then resorts to instinctive methods of getting out. Its actions are exactly what would be expected of an animal in whom the sense-impression aroused the impulse imperfectly, or weakly, or intermittently, but are not at all like the actions of one who felt, "I used to get out of this box by pulling that loop down." In fact, the record of No. 10 given on page 139 seems to be final on this point.   If at any time in the course of the 50 trials it had *remembered* that 'I will not feed them' meant 'no fish,' it would thenceforth have failed to react.   It would have stopped short in the 'yes' reactions, instead of gradually decreasing their percentage.   'Memory' in animals, if one still chooses to use the word, is *permanence of associations*, not the presence of an idea of an experience attributed to the past.

To this proposition two corollaries may be added.   First, these phenomena of incomplete forgetfulness extend the evidence that animals do not have a stock of independent ideas, the return of which, plus past associates, equals memory.   Second, there is, properly speaking, no continuity in their mental streams.   The present thought does not clutch the past to its bosom or hold the future in its womb. The animal's self is not a being 'looking before and after,' but a direct practical association of feelings and impulses. So far as experiences come continuously, they may be said to form a continuous mental life, but there is no continuity imposed from within.   The feelings of its own body are always present, and impressions from outside may come as they come to us.   When the habit of attending to the elements of its associations and raising them up into the life of free ideas is acquired, these permanent bodily associations may become the basis of a feeling of self-hood and the trains of ideas may be felt as a continuous life.

INHIBITION OF INSTINCTS BY HABIT

One very important result of association remains to be considered, its inhibition of instincts and previous associations.   An animal who has become habituated to getting out of a box by pulling a loop and opening the door will do so even though the hole in the top of the box be uncovered, whereas, if, in early trials, you had left any such hole, he would have taken the instinctive way and crawled through it. Instances of this sort of thing are well-nigh ubiquitous. It is a tremendous factor in animal life, and the strongest instincts may thus be annulled. The phenomenon has been already recognized in the literature of the subject, a convenient account being found in James' 'Psychology,' Vol. II, pages 394–397. In addition to such accounts, one may note that the influence of association is exerted in two ways. The instinct may wane by not being used, because the animal forms the habit of meeting the situation in a different way, or it may be actually inhibited. An instance of the former sort is found in the history of a cat which learns to pull a loop and so escape from a box whose top is covered by a board nailed over it. If, after enough trials, you remove a piece of the board covering the box, the cat, when put in, will still pull the loop instead of crawling out through the opening thus made. But, at any time, if she happens to notice the hole, she *may* make use of it. An instance of the second sort is that of a chick which has been put on a box with a wire screen at its edge, preventing her from jumping directly down, as she would instinctively do, and forcing her to jump to another box on one side of it and thence down. In the experiments which I made, the chick was prevented by a second screen from jumping directly from the second box also. That is, if in the accompanying figure, A is a box 34 inches high, B a box 25 inches high, C a box 16 inches high, and D the pen with the food and other chicks, the subject had to go A–B–C–D. The chick tried at first to get through the screen, pecked at it and ran up and down along it, looking at the chicks below and seeking for a hole to get through. Finally

it jumped to B and, after a similar process, to C. After
enough trials it forms the habit and when put on A goes

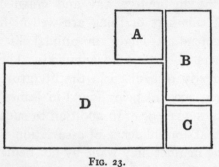

FIG. 23.

immediately to B, then
to C and down. Now
if, after 75 or 80 trials,
you take away the
screens, giving the chick
a free chance to go to D
from either A or B, and
then put it on A, the
following   phenomenon
appears. The chick goes
up to the edge, looks over, walks up and down it for a while,
still looking down at the chicks below, and then goes and
jumps to B as habit has taught it to do. The same actions
take place on B. No matter how clearly the chick sees
the chance to jump to D, it does not do so. The impulse has
been truly inhibited. It is not the mere habit of going the
other way, but the impossibility of going *that* way. In one
case I observed a chick in whom the instinct was all but, yet
not quite, inhibited. When tried without the screen, it went
up to the edge to look over *nine times*, and at last, after
seven minutes, did jump straight down.

ATTENTION

I have presupposed throughout one function which it
will be well to now recognize explicitly, attention. As
usual, attention emphasizes and facilitates the process
which it accompanies. Unless the sense-impression is
focussed by attention, it will not be associated with the
act which comes later. Unless two differing boxes are attended to, there will be no difference in the reactions to

them. The really effective part of animal consciousness, then, as of human, is the part which is attended to; attention is the ruler of animal as well as human mind.

But in giving attention its deserts we need not forget that it is not here comparable to the whole of human attention. Our attention to the other player and the ball in a game of tennis *is* like the animal's attention, but our attention to a passage in Hegel, or the memory which flits through our mind, or the song we hear, or the player we idly watch, is *not*. There ought, I think, to be a separate name for attention when working for immediate practical associations. It is a different species from that which holds objects so that we may define them, think about them, remember them, etc., and the difference is, as our previous sentence shows, not that between voluntary and involuntary attention. The cat watching me for signs of my walking to the cage with fish is not in the condition of the man watching a ball game, but in that of the player watching the ball speeding toward him. There is a notable difference in the permanence of the impression. The man watching the game can remember just how that fly was hit and how the fielder ran for it, though he bestowed only a slight quantity of attention on the matter, while the fielder may attend to the utmost to the ball and yet not remember at all how it came or how he ran for it. The one sort of attention leads you to *think* about a thing, the other to *act* with reference to it. We must be careful to remember that when we say that the cat attended to what was said, we do not mean that he thereby established an idea of it. Animals are not proved to form separate ideas of sense-impressions because they attend to them, for the kind of attention they give is the kind which, when given by men, results in practical associations, not in establishing ideas of objects. If attention rendered clear the idea, we should not have the phenomena of incomplete forgetfulness lately mentioned. The animal would get a definite idea of just the exact thing done and would do it or nothing. The human development of attention is in closest connection with the acquisition of a stock of free ideas.

SOCIAL CONSCIOUSNESS

Besides attention there is another topic somewhat apart from our general one, which yet deserves a few words. It concerns animals' social consciousness, their consciousness of the feelings of their fellows. Do animals, for example, when they see others feeding, feel that the others are feeling pleasure? Do they, when they fight, feel that the other feels pain? So level-headed a thinker as Lloyd Morgan has said that they do, but the conduct of my animals would seem to show that they did not. For it has given us good reason to suppose that they do not possess *any* stock of isolated ideas, much less any abstracted, inferred, or transferred ideas. These ideas of others' feelings imply a power to transfer states felt in oneself to another and realize them as there. Now it seems that any ability to thus transfer and realize an idea ought to carry with it an ability to form a transferred association, to imitate. If the animal realizes the mental states of the other animal who before his eyes pulls the string, goes out through the door, and eats fish, he ought to form the association, 'impulse to pull string, pleasure of eating fish.' This we saw the animal could not do.

In fact, pleasure in another, pain in another, is not a sense-presentation or a representation or feeling of an object of any sort, but rather a 'meaning,' a feeling '*of the fact that*.' It can exist only as something thought *about*.

It is never 'a bit of direct experience,' but an abstraction from our own life referred to that of another.

I fancy that these feelings of others' feelings may be connected pretty closely with imitation, and for that reason may begin to appear in the monkeys. There we have some fair evidence for their presence in the tricks which monkeys play on each other. Such feelings seem the natural explanation of the apparently useless tail-pullings and such like which make up the attractions of the monkey cage. These may, however, be instinctive forms of play-activity or merely examples of the general tendency of the monkeys to fool with everything.

INTERACTION

I hope it will not be thought impertinent if from the standpoint of this research I add a word about a general psychological problem, the problem of interaction. I have spoken all along of the connection between the situation and a certain impulse and act being stamped in when pleasure results from the act and stamped out when it doesn't. In this fact, which is undeniable, lies a problem which Lloyd Morgan has frequently emphasized. *How are pleasurable results able to burn in and render predominant the association which led to them?* This is perhaps the greatest problem of both human and animal psychology. Unfortunately in human psychology it has been all tangled up with the problems of free will, mental activity, voluntary attention, the creation of novel acts, and almost everything else. In our experiments we get the data which give rise to the problem, in a very elementary form.

It should first be noted about the *fact* that the pleasure does not burn in an impulse and act themselves, but an impulse and act *as connected with that particular situation*. No cat ever goes around clawing, clawing, clawing all the time, because clawing in these boxes has resulted in pleasure. Secondly, the connection thus stamped in is *not contemporaneous, but prior to* the pleasure. So much for the fact; now for the explanation. I do not wish to rehearse or add to the arguments with which so many pages have been already filled by scientists and philosophers both. What we need most is not argument, but accurate accounts of the mental fact and of the brain-process. But I do wish to say to the parallelist, what has not to my knowledge been said, that if he presupposes, to account for this fact, a ' physical analogue of the hedonic consciousness,' it is his bounden duty to first show how any motion in any neurone or group of neurones in the nervous system can possess this power of stamping in any current which causes it. For no one would, from our present knowledge of the brain, judge *a priori* that any motion in any part of it could be conceived which should be thus regnant over all the others. And next he must show the possibility of the current which represents the association being the excitant of the regnant motion in a manner direct enough for the purpose.

I wish also to say that whoever thinks that, going along with the current which parallels the association, there is an accompanying minor current, which parallels the pleasure and which stamps in the first current when present with it, flies directly in the face of the facts. *There is no pleasure along with the association. The pleasure does not come until after the association is done and gone.* It is caused by no such minor current, but by the excitation of peripheral sense-organs when freedom from confinement is realized or food is secured. Of course, the notion of such a secondary subcurrent is mythology, anyway.

To the interactionist I would say: "Do not any more repeat in tiresome fashion that consciousness *does* alter movement, but get to work and show when, where, in what forms and to what degrees it does so. Then, even if it turns out to have been a physical parallel that did the work, you will, at least, have the credit of attaining the best knowledge about the results and their conditions, even though you mis-named the factor."

Besides this contribution to general psychology, I think we may safely offer one to pedagogical science. At least some of our results possess considerable pedagogical inter-est. The fundamental form of intellection, the association-process in animals, is one, we decided, which requires the personal experience of the animal in all its elements. The association cannot be taught by putting the animal through it or giving it a chance to imitate. Now every observant teacher realizes how often the cleverest explanation and the best models for imitation fail. Yet often, in such cases, a pupil, if somehow enticed to do the thing, even without comprehension of what it means, even without any real knowledge of what he is doing, will finally get hold of it. So, also, in very many kinds of knowledge, the pupil who does anything from imitation, or who does anything from being put through it, fails to get a real and permanent mas-tery of the thing. I am sure that with a certain type of mind the only way to teach fractions in algebra, for example, is to get the pupil to do, do, do. I am inclined to think that in many individuals certain things cannot be learned save by actual performance. And I think it is often a fair question, when explanation, imitation and actual performance are all possible methods, which is the best. We are here alongside the foundations of mental life, and this hitherto unsuspected law of animal mind may prevail in human mind to an extent hitherto unknown. The best way with children may often be, in the pompous words of an animal trainer, ' to arrange everything in connection with the trick so that the animal will be compelled by the laws of his own nature to perform it.'

This does not at all imply that I think, as a present school of scientists seem to, that because a certain thing *has been* in phylogeny we ought to repeat it in ontogeny. Heaven knows that Dame Nature herself in ontogeny abbreviates and skips and distorts the order of the appearance of organs and functions, and for the best of reasons. We ought to make an effort, as she does, to omit the useless and anti-quated and get to the best and most useful as soon as possible ; we ought to change what *is* to what *ought to be*, as far as we can. And I would not advocate this animal-like method of learning in place of the later ones unless it does the same work better. I simply suggest that in many cases where at present its use is never dreamed of, it may be a good method. As the fundamental form of intellection, every student of *theoretical* pedagogy ought to take it into account.

There is one more contribution, this time to anthropology. If the method of trial and error, with accidental success, be the method of acquiring associations among the animals, the slow progress of primitive man, the long time between stone age and iron age, for instance, becomes suggestive. Primi-tive man probably acquired knowledge by just this process, aided possibly by imitation. At any rate, progress was not by seeing through things, but by accidentally hitting upon them. Very possibly an investigation of the history of primitive man and of the present life of savages in the light of the results of this research might bring out old facts in a new and profitable way.

Comparative psychology has, in the light of this research,

two tasks of prime importance. One is to study the passage of the child mind from a life of immediately practical associations to the life of free ideas; the other is to find out how far the anthropoid primates advance toward a similar passage, and to ascertain accurately what faint beginnings or preparations for such an advance the early mammalian stock may be supposed to have had. In this latter connection I think it will be of the utmost importance to bear in mind the possibility that *the present anthropoid primates may be mentally degenerate.* Their present aimless activity and incessant, but largely useless, curiosity may be the degenerated vestiges of such a well-directed activity and useful curiosity as led *homo sapiens* to important practical discoveries, such as the use of tools, the art of making fire, etc. It is even a remote possibility that their chattering is a *relic* of something like language, not a *beginning* of such. Comparative psychology should use the phenomena of the monkey mind of to-day to find out what the primitive mind from which man's sprung off was like. That is the important thing to get at, and the question whether the present monkey mind has not gone back instead of ahead is an all-important question. A natural and perhaps sufficient cause of degeneracy would be arboreal habits. The animal that found a means of survival in his muscles might well lose the means before furnished by his brain.

To these disconnected remarks still another must be added, addressed this time to the anecdote school. Some member of it who has chanced to read this may feel like saying: "This experimental work is all very well. Your cats and dogs represent, it is true, specimens from the top stratum of animal intelligence, and your negations, based on their conduct, may be authoritative so far as concerns the average, typical mammalian mind. But our anecdotes do not claim to be stories of the conduct of the average or type, but of those exceptional individuals who have begun to attain higher powers. And, if even a few dogs and cats have these higher powers, our contention is, in a modified form, upheld." To all this I agree, provided the anecdote school now realize just what sort of a position they hold. They are clearly in pretty much the same position as spiritualists. Their anecdotes are on pretty much the same level as the anecdotes of thought-transference, materializations of spirits, supernormal knowledge, etc. Not in quite the same position, for far greater care has been given by the Psychical Research Society to establishing the criteria of authenticity, to insuring good observation, to explaining by normal psychology all that can be so explained, in the case of the latter than the anecdote school has done in the case of the former. The off-hand explanation of certain anecdotes by invoking reason, or imitation, or recognition, or feelings of qualities, is on a par with the explanation of trance-phenomena and such like by invoking the spirits of dead people. I do not deny that we may get lawfully a supernormal psychology, or that the supernormal acts it finds may turn out to be explained by these functions which I have denied to the normal animal mind. But I must soberly declare that I think there is less likelihood that such functions are the explanation of animal acts than that the existence of the spirits of dead people is the true explanation of the automatisms of spiritualistic phenomena. So much for the anecdote school, if it calls itself by its right name and pretends only to give an *abnormal* animal psychology. The sad fact has been that it has always pushed forward these exceptions as the essential phenomena of animal mind. It has built up a general psychology from abnormal data. It is like an anatomy written from observations on dime-museum freaks.

CONCLUSION

I do not think it is advisable here, at the close of this paper, to give a summary of its results. The paper itself is really only such a summary with the most important evidence, for the extent of territory covered and the need of brevity have prevented completeness in explanation or illustration. If the reader cares here, at the end, to have the broadest possible statement of our conclusions and will take the pains to supply the right meaning, we might say that our work has described a method, crude but promising, and has made the beginning of an exact estimate of just what associations, simple and compound, an animal can form, how quickly he forms them, and how long he retains them. It has described the method of formation, and, on the condition that our subjects were representative, has rejected reason, comparison or inference, perception of similarity, and imitation. It has denied the existence in animal consciousness of any important stock of free ideas or impulses, and so has denied that animal association is homologous with the association of human psychology. It has homologized it with a certain limited form of human association. It has proposed, as necessary steps in the evolution of human faculty, a vast increase in the number of associations, signs of which appear in the primates, and a freeing of the elements thereof into independent existence. It has given us an increased insight into various mental processes. It has convinced the writer, if not the reader, that the old speculations about what an animal could do, what it thought, and how what it thought grew into what human beings think, were a long way from the truth, and *not on the road to it*.

Finally, I wish to say that, although the changes proposed

in the conception of mental development have been suggested somewhat fragmentarily and in various connections, that has not been done because I think them unimportant. On the contrary, I think them of the utmost importance. I believe that our best service has been to show that animal intellection is made up of a lot of specific connections, whose elements are restricted to them, and which subserve practical ends *directly,* and to homologize it with the intellection involved in such human associations as regulate the conduct of a man playing tennis. The fundamental phenomenon which I find presented in animal consciousness is one which can harden into inherited connections and reflexes, on the one hand, and thus connect naturally with a host of the phenomena of animal life; on the other hand, it emphasizes the fact that our mental life has grown up as a mediation between stimulus and reaction. The old view of human consciousness is that it is built up out of elementary sensations, that very minute bits of consciousness come first and gradually get built up into the complex web. It looks for the beginnings of consciousness to *little* feelings. This our view abolishes and declares that the progress is not from little and simple to big and complicated, but from direct connections to indirect connections in which a stock of isolated elements plays a part, is from 'pure experience' or undifferentiated feelings, to discrimination, on the one hand, to generalizations, abstractions, on the other. If, as seems probable, the primates display a vast increase of associations, and a stock of free-swimming ideas, our view gives to the line of descent a meaning which it never could have so long as the question was the vague one of more or less 'intelligence.' It will, I hope, when supported by an investigation of the mental life of the primates and of the period in child life when these directly practical associations become overgrown by a rapid luxuriance of free ideas, show us the real history of the origin of human faculty. It turns out apparently that a modest study of the facts of association in animals has given us a working hypothesis for a comparative psychology.

CHAPTER III

THE INSTINCTIVE REACTIONS OF YOUNG CHICKS [1]

THE data to be presented in this article were obtained in the course of a series of experiments conducted in connection with the psychological laboratory of Harvard University during the year 1896–1897. About sixty chicks were used as subjects. In general their experiences were entirely under my control from birth. Where this was not true, the conditions of their life previous to the experiments were known, and were such as would have had no influence in determining the quality of their reactions in the particular experiments to which they were subjected. It is not worth while to recount the means taken so to regulate the chick's environment that his experience along certain lines should be in its entirety known to the observer and that consequently his inherited abilities could be surely differentiated. The nature of the experiments will, in most cases, be such that little suspicion of the influence of education by experience will be possible. In the other cases I will mention the particular means then taken to prevent such influence.

Some of my first experiments were on color vision in chicks from 18 to 30 hours old, just old enough to move about readily and to be hungry. On backgrounds of white and black cardboard were pasted pieces of colored paper about 2 mm. square. On each background there were six

[1] This chapter appeared originally in the *Psychological Review*, Vol. VI, No. 3.

of these pieces, — one each of yellow, red, orange, green, blue and black (on the white ground) or white (on the black). They were in a row about half an inch apart. The chicks had been in darkness for all but three or four hours of their life so far. During those few hours the incubator had been illuminated and the chicks had that much chance to learn color.

The eight chicks were put, one at a time, on the sheet of cardboard facing the colored spots. Count was kept of the number of times that they pecked at each spot and, of course, they were watched to see whether they would peck at all at random. In the experiments with the white background all the colors were reacted to (*i.e.* pecked at) except black (but the letters on a newspaper were pecked at by the same chicks the same day). One of the chicks pecked at all five, one at four, three at three, one at two and one at yellow only. These differences are due probably to accidental position or movements. Taking the sums of the reactions to each color-spot we get the following table : —

I

	TIMES REACTED TO	TOTAL NUMBER OF PECKS[1]
Red	12	31
Yellow	9	21
Orange.	6	34
Green	5	11
Blue	1	3

I should attach no importance whatever to the quantitative estimate given in the table. The only fact of value so

[1] This double rating is necessary because of the fact that the chick often gives several distinct pecks in a single reaction. The 'times reacted to' mean the number of different times that the chicks noticed the color.

far is the evidence that from the first the chick reacts to all colors. In no case was there any random pecking at the white surface of the cardboard.

On a black background the same chicks reacted to all the colors.

II is a table of the results.

II

	Times Reacted to	Total Number of Pecks
White	6	19
Blue	4	11
Red	4	8
Green	4	4
Orange	2	7
Yellow	2	4

In other experiments chicks were tried with green spots on a red ground, red spots on a green ground, yellow spots on an orange ground, green spots on a blue ground, and black spots on a white ground. All were reacted to. Thus, what is apparently a long and arduous task to the child is heredity's gift to the chick. It is conceivable, though to me incredible, that what the chick reacts to is not the color, but the very minute elevation of the spot. My spots were made so that they were only the thickness of thin paper above pasteboard. Any one who cares to resort to the theory that this elevation caused the reaction can settle the case by using color-spots absolutely level with the surface.[1]

[1] The crude experiments reported in this and the preceding paragraphs were not made to test the presence of color vision proper, that is, of differentiation of two colors of the same brightness, but only to ascertain how chicks reacted to ordinary colored objects. It was, however, almost certain from the relative frequency of the reactions that the intensity factor was not the cause of the response. For example, if it had been, black on white and yellow on black should have been pecked at oftener.

Instinctive Reactions to Distance, Direction, Size, etc.

I have purposely chosen this awkward heading rather than the simple one, Space-Perception, because I do not wish to imply that there is in the young chick such consciousness of space-facts as there is in human beings. All that will be shown here is that he reacts appropriately in the presence of space-facts, reacts in a fashion which would in the case of a man go with genuine perception of space.

If one puts a chick on top of a box in sight of his fellows below, the chick will regulate his conduct by the height of the box. To be definite, we may take the average chick of about 95 hours. If the height is less than 10 inches, he will jump down as soon as you put him up. At 16 inches he will jump in from 5 seconds to 3 or 4 minutes. At 22 inches he will still jump down, but after more hesitation. At 27½ inches 6 chicks out of eight at this age jumped within 5 minutes. At 39 inches the chick *will* NOT *jump down*. The numerical values given here would, of course, vary with the health, development, hunger and degree of lonesomeness of the chick. All that they are supposed to show is that at any given age the chick without experience of heights regulates his conduct rather accurately in accord with the space-fact of distance which confronts him. The chick does not peck at objects remote from him, does not, for instance, confuse a bird a score of feet away with a fly near by, or try to get the moon inside his bill. Moreover, he reacts in pecking with considerable accuracy at the very start. Lloyd Morgan has noted that in his very first efforts the chick often fails to seize the object, though he hits it, and on this ground has denied the perfection of the instinct. But, as a matter of fact, the pecking reaction may be as perfect at birth as it is

after 10 or 12 days' experience.   It certainly is not perfect
then.   I took nine chicks from 10 to 14 days old and placed
them one at a time on a clear surface over which were scattered grains of cracked wheat (the food they had been eating in this same way for a week) and watched the accuracy
of their pecking.   Out of 214 objects pecked at, 159 were
seized, 55 *were not*.   Out of the 159 that were seized, *only*
116 were seized on the first peck, 25 on the second, 16 on the
third, and the remaining two on the fourth.   Of the 55 that
were not successfully seized, 31 were pecked at only once,
10 twice, 10 three times, 3 four times and 1 five times.   I
fancy one would find that adult fowls would show by no
means a perfect record.   So long as chicks with ten days'
experience fail to seize on the first trial 45 per cent of the
time, it is hardly fair to argue against the perfection of the
instinct on the ground of failures to seize during the first day.

The chick's practical appreciation of space-facts is seen
further in his attempts to escape when confined.   Put chicks
only twenty or thirty hours old in a box with walls three or
four inches high and they will react to the perpendicularity
of the confining walls by trying to jump over them.   In fact,
in the ways he moves, the directions he takes and the objects
he reacts to, the chicken has prior to experience the power
of appropriate reaction to colors and facts of all three dimen-
sions.

INSTINCTIVE MUSCULAR COÖRDINATIONS

In the acts already described we see fitting coördinations
at work in the chick's reactions to space-facts.   A few more
samples may be given.   In jumping down from heights the
chick does not walk off or fall off (save rarely), but jumps
off.   He meets the situation "loneliness on a small eminence"
by walking around the edge and peering down ; he meets the

situation "sight of fellow chicks below " by (after an amount of hesitation varying roughly with the height) jumping off, holding his stubby wings out and keeping right side up. He lands on his feet almost every time and generally very cleverly. A four days' chick will jump down a distance eight times his own height without hurting himself a bit. If one takes a chick two or three weeks old who has never had a chance to jump up or down, and puts him in a box with walls three times the height of the chick's back, he will find that the chick will jump, or rather fly, nearly, if not quite, over the wall, flapping his wings lustily and holding on to the edge with his neck while he clambers over. Chicks one day old will, in about 57 per cent of the cases, balance themselves for five or six seconds when placed on a stiff perch. If eight or nine days old, they will, though never before on any perch or anything like one, balance perfectly for a minute or more. The muscular coördination required is invoked immediately when the chick feels the situation "feet on a perch." The *strength* is lacking in the first few days. From the fifth or sixth day on chicks are also able (their ability increases with age) to balance themselves on a slowly swinging perch.

Another complex coördination is seen in the somewhat remarkable instinct of swimming. Chicks only a day or two old will, if tossed into a pond, head straight for the shore and swim rapidly to it. It is impossible to compare their movements in so doing with those of ducklings, for the chick is agitated, paddles his feet very fast and swims to get out, not for swimming's sake. Dr. Bashford Dean, of Columbia University, has suggested to me that the movements may not be those of swimming, but only of running. At all events, they are utterly different from those of an adult fowl. In the case of the adult there is no vigorous instinct to strike out toward the shore. The hen may try to fly back into the boat if it is dropped overboard, and whether dropped in or slung in from the shore, will float about aimlessly for a while and only very slowly reach the shore. The movements the chick makes do look to be such as trying to run in water might lead to, but it is hard to see why a hen shouldn't run to get out of cold water as well as a chick. If, on the other hand, the actions of the chick are due to a real swimming instinct, it is easy to see that, being unused, the instinct might wane as the animal grew up.

Such instinctive coördinations as these, together with the walking, running, preening of feathers, stretching out of leg backward, scratching the head, etc., noted by other observers, make the infant chick a very interesting contrast to the infant man. That the helplessness of the child is a sacrifice to plasticity, instability and consequent power to develop we all know; but one begins to realize how much of a sacrifice when one sees what twenty-one days of embryonic life do for the chick brain. And one cannot help wondering whether some of the space-perception we trace to experience, some of the coördinations which we attribute to a gradual development from random, accidentally caused movements may not be more or less definitely provided for by the child's inherited brain structure. Walking has been found to be instinctive; why not other things?

INSTINCTIVE EMOTIONAL REACTIONS

The only experiments to which I wish to refer at length under this heading are some concerning the chick's instinctive fears. Before describing them, it may be well to mention their general bearing on the results obtained by Spalding and Morgan. They corroborate Morgan's decision that no well-defined specific fears are present; that the fears of young chicks are of strange moving objects in general, shock in general, strange sounds in general. On the other hand, no such general disturbances of the chick's environment led to such well-marked reactions as Spalding described. And so when Morgan thinks that such behavior as Spalding witnessed on the part of the chick that heard the hawk's cry demands for its explanation nothing more than a general fear of strange sounds, my experiments do not allow me to agree with him. If Spalding really saw the conduct which he says the chick exhibited on the third day of its life in the presence of man, and later at the stimulus of the sight or sound of the hawk, there are specific reactions. For the running, crouching, silence, quivering, etc., that one gets by yelling, banging doors, tormenting a violin, throwing hats, bottles, or brushes at the chick is never anything like so pronounced and never lasts one tenth as long as it did with Spalding's chicks. But, as to the fear of man, Spalding must have been deluded. In the second, third and fourth days there is no such reaction to the sight of man as he thought he saw. Miss Hattie E. Hunt, in the *American Journal of Psychology*, Vol. IX., No. 1, asserts that there is no instinctive fear of a cat. Morgan did not find such. I myself put chicks of 2, 5, 9 and 17 days (different individuals each time, 11 in all) in the presence of a cat. They showed no fear, but went on eating as if there was nothing about. The cat was still, or only slowly moving. I further put a young kitten (eight inches long) in the pen with chicks. He felt of them with his paw, and walked around among them for five or ten minutes, yet they showed no fear (nor did he instinctively attack them). If, however, you let a cat jump at chicks in real earnest, they will not stay to be eaten, but will manifest fear — at least chicks three to four weeks old will. I did not try this experiment with chicks at different ages, because it seemed rather cruel and degrading to the experimenter. When in the case of the older chicks nature happened to make the experiment, it was hard to decide whether there was more violent fear of the jumping cat than there was when one threw a basket or football into the pen.· There was not very much more.

We may now proceed to a brief recital of the facts shown by the experiments in so far as they are novel. It should be remembered throughout that in every case chicks of different ages were tested so as to demonstrate transitory instincts if such existed, *e.g.*, the presence of a fear of flame was tested with chicks 59 and 60, one day old, 30 and 32, two days old, 21 and 22, three days old, 23 and 24, seven days old, 27 and 29, nine days old, 16 and 19, eleven days old, and so on up to twenty-days-old chicks. By thus using different subjects at each trial one, of course, eliminates any influence of experience.

The first notable fact is that there develops in the first month a general fear of novel objects in motion. For four or five days there seems to be no such. You may throw a hat or slipper or shaving mug at a chick of that age, and he will do no more than get out of the way of it. But a twenty-five-days-old chick will generally chirr, run and crouch for five or ten seconds. My records show this sort of thing beginning about the tenth day, but it is about ten days more before it is very marked. In general, also, the reaction is more pronounced if many chicks are together, and is then displayed earlier (only two at a time were taken in the experiments the results of which have just been quoted). Thus the reaction is to some degree a social performance, the presence of other chicks combining with the strange object to increase the vigor of the reaction. Chicks ordinarily scatter apart when they thus run from an object.

One witnesses a similar gradual growth of the fear of man (not as such probably, but merely as a large moving object). For four or five days you can jump at the chick, grab at it with your hands, etc., without disturbing it in the least. A chick twenty days old, however, although he has never been touched or approached by a man, and in some cases never seen one except as the daily bringer of food, and has never been in any way injured by any large moving object of any sort, will run from you if you try to catch him or even get very near him. There is, however, even then, nothing like the utter fear described by Spalding.

Up to thirty days there was no fear of a mocking bird into whose cage the chicks were put, no fear of a stuffed hawk or a stuffed owl (kept stationary). Chicks try to escape from water (even though warmed to the temperature of their bodies) from the very first. Up to forty days there appears no marked waning of the instinct. They did not show any emotional reaction to the flame produced by six candles stuck closely together. From the start they react instinctively to confinement, to loneliness, to bodily restraint, but their feeling in these cases would better be called discomfort than fear. From the 10th or 12th to the 20th day, and probably later and very possibly earlier, one notices in chicks a general avoidance of open places. Turn them out in your study and they will not go out into the middle of the room, but will cling to the edges, go under chairs, around table legs and along the walls. One sees nothing of the sort up through the fourth day. Some experiments with feeding hive bees to the chicks are interesting in connection with the following statement by Lloyd Morgan: "One of my chicks, three or four days old, snapped up a hive bee and ran off with it. Then he dropped it, shook his head much and often, and wiped his bill repeatedly. I do not think

he had been stung : *probably he tasted the poison"* ('Introduction to Comparative Psychology,' p. 86). I fed seven
bees apiece to three chicks from ten to twenty days old.
They ate them all greedily, first smashing them down on the
ground violently in a rather dexterous manner. Apparently
this method of treatment is peculiar to the object. Chicks
three days old did not eat the bees. Some pecked at
them, but none would snap them up, and when the bee
approached, they sometimes sounded the danger note.

Finally an account may be given of the reaction of chicks
at different ages, up to twenty-six days, to loud sounds.
These were the sounds made by clapping the hands, slam-
ming a door, whistling sharply, banging a tin pan on the
floor, mewing like a cat, playing a violin, thumping a coal
scuttle with a shovel, etc. Two chicks were together in
each experiment. Three fourths of the times no effect
was produced. On the other occasions there was some running or crouching or, at least, starting to run or crouch;
but, as was said, nothing like what Spalding reports as the
reaction to the 'cheep' of the hawk. It is interesting to
notice that the two most emphatic reactions were to the
imitation mew. One time a chick ran wildly, chirring, and
then crouched and stayed still until I had counted 105. The
other time a chick crouched and stayed still until I counted
40. But the other chick with them did not; and in a dozen
other cases the 'meaw' had no effect.

I think that the main interest of most of these experiments
is the proof they afford that instinctive reactions are not
necessarily definite, perfectly appropriate and unvarying responses to accurately sensed and, so to speak, estimated
stimuli. The old notion that instinct was a God-given substitute for reason left us an unhappy legacy in the shape
of the tendency to think of all inherited powers of reaction as

definite particular acts invariably done in the presence of certain equally definite situations. Such an act as the spider's web-spinning might be a stock example. Of course, there are many such instinctive reactions in which a well-defined act follows a well-defined stimulus with the regularity and precision with which the needle approaches the magnet. But our experiments show that there are acts just as truly instinctive, depending in just the same way on inherited brain-structure, but characterized by being vague, irregular, and to some extent dissimilar, reactions to vague, complex situations.

The same stimulus doesn't always produce just the same effect, doesn't produce precisely the same effect in all individuals. The chick's brain is evidently prepared in a general way to react more or less appropriately to certain stimuli, and these reactions are among the most important of its instincts or inherited functions. But yet one cannot take these and find them always and everywhere. This helps us further to realize the danger of supposing that in observation of animals you can depend on a rigid uniformity. One would never suppose because one boy twirled his thumb when asked a question that all boys of that age did. But naturalists have been ready to believe that because one young animal made a certain response to a certain stimulus, the thing was an instinct common to all in precisely that same form. But a loud sound may make one chick run, another crouch, another give the danger call, and another do nothing whatever.

In closing this article I may speak of one instinct which shows itself clearly from at least as early as the sixth day, which is preparatory to the duties of adult life and of no other use whatsoever. It is interesting in connection with the general matter of animal play. The phenomenon is as follows : The chicks are feeding quietly when suddenly two chicks rush at each other, face each other a moment and then go about their business. This thing keeps up and grows into the ordinary combat of roosters. It is rather a puzzle on any theory that an instinct needed so late should begin to develop so early.

CHAPTER IV

A NOTE ON THE PSYCHOLOGY OF FISHES [1]

NUMEROUS facts witness in a vague way to the ability of fishes to profit by experience and fit their behavior to situations unprovided for by their innate nervous equipment. All the phenomena shown by fishes as a result of taming are, of course, of this sort. But such facts have not been exact enough to make clear the mental or nervous processes involved in such behavior, or simple enough to be available as demonstrations of such processes. It seemed desirable to obtain evidence which should demonstrate both the fact and the process of learning or intelligent activity in the case of fishes and demonstrate them so readily that any student could possess the evidence first hand.

Through the kindness of the officials of the United States Fish Commission at Woods Holl, especially of the director, Dr. Bumpus, I was able to test the efficiency of some simple experiments directed toward this end. The common Fundulus was chosen as a convenient subject, and also because of the neurological interest attaching to the formation of intelligent habits by a vertebrate whose forebrain lacks a cortex.

The fishes studied were kept in an aquarium (about 4 feet long by 2 feet wide, with a water depth of about 9 inches) represented by Fig. 24. The space at one end, as repre-

[1] This chapter appeared originally in the *American Naturalist*, Vol. XXXIII, No. 396.

sented by the lines in the figure, was shaded from the sun by
a cover, and all food was dropped in at this end.   Along each

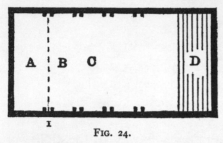

FIG. 24.

side of the aquarium were
fastened simple pairs of
cleats, allowing the ex-
perimenter to put across
it partitions of wood,
glass or wire screening.
One of these in position
is shown in the figure by

the dotted line.   These partitions were made each with an
opening, as shown in Fig. 25.   If now we cause the fish to
leave his shady corner and swim up to
the sunny end by putting a slide (without any opening) in behind him at *D*
and moving it gently from *D* to *A* and
then place, say slide *I*, across the
aquarium at 1, we shall have a chance
to observe the animal's behavior to
good purpose.

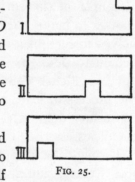

FIG. 25.

This fish dislikes the sunlight and
tries to get back to *D*.   He reacts to
the situation in which he finds himself
by swimming against the screen, bumping against it here
and there along the bottom.   He may stop and remain
still for a while.   He will occasionally rise up toward the
top of the water, especially while swimming up and down
the length of the screen.   When he happens to rise up to the
top at the right-hand end, he has a clear path in front of him
and swims to *D* and feels more comfortable.

If, after he has enjoyed the shade fifteen minutes or more,
you again confine him in *A*, and keep on doing so six or eight
times a day for a day or so, you will find that he swims

against the screen less and less, swims up and down along it fewer and fewer times, stays still less and less, until finally his only act is to go to the right-hand side, rise up, and swim out. In correspondence with this change in behavior you will find a very marked decrease in the time he takes to escape. The fish has clearly profited by his experience and modified his conduct to suit a situation for which his innate nervous equipment did not definitely provide. He has, in common language, *learned* to get out.

This particular experiment was repeated with a number of individuals. Another experiment was made, using three slides, *II, III*, and another, requiring the fish to find his way from *A* to *B*, *B* to *C*, and from *C* to *D*. The results of these and still others show exactly the same general mental process as does the one described — a process which I have discussed at length elsewhere.

Whatever interest there is in the demonstration in the case of the bony fishes of the same process which accounts for so much of the behavior of the higher vertebrates may be left to the neurologists. The value of the experiment, if any, to most students will perhaps be the extreme simplicity of the method, the ease of administering it, and its possibilities. By using long aquaria, one can study the formation of very complex series of acts and see to what extent any fish can carry the formation of such series. By proper arrangements the delicacy of discrimination of the fish in any respect may be tested. The artificiality of the surroundings may, of course, be avoided when desirable.

CHAPTER V

The Mental Life of the Monkeys; an Experimental Study [1]

The literary form of this monograph is not at all satisfactory to its author. Compelled by practical considerations to present the facts in a limited space, he has found it necessary to omit explanation, illustration and many rhetorical aids to clearness and emphasis. For the same reason detailed accounts of the administration of the experiments have not always been given. In many places theoretical matters are discussed with a curtness that savors of dogmatism. In general when a theoretical point has appeared justified by the evidence given, I have, to economize space, withheld further evidence.

There is, however, to some extent a real fitness in the lack of clearness, completeness and finish in the monograph. For the behavior of the monkeys, by virtue of their inconstant attention, decided variability of performance, and generally aimless, unforetellable conduct would be falsely represented in any clean-cut, unambiguous, emphatic exposition. The most striking testimony to the mental advance of the monkeys over the dogs and cats is given by the difficulty of making clear emphatic statements about them.

---

[1] This chapter appeared originally as Monograph Supplement No. 15 to the *Psychological Review*.

INTRODUCTION

The work to be described in this paper is a direct continuation of the work done by the author in 1897–1898 and described in Monograph Supplement No. 8 of the *Psychological Review* under the heading, 'Animal Intelligence; an Experimental Study of the Associative Processes in Animals.'[1] This monograph affords by far the best introduction to the present discussion, and I shall therefore assume an acquaintance with it on the part of my readers.

It will be remembered that evidence was there given that ordinary mammals, barring the primates, did not infer or compare, did not imitate in the sense of 'learning to do an act from seeing it done,' did not learn various simple acts from being put through them, showed no signs of having in connection with the bulk of their performances any mental images. Their method of learning seemed to be the gradual selection of certain acts in certain situations by reason of the satisfaction they brought. Quantitative estimates of this gradualness were given for a number of dogs and cats. Nothing has appeared since the 'Experimental Study' to negate any of these conclusions in the author's mind. The work of Kline and Small[2] on rodents shows the same general aspect of mammalian mentality.

Adult human beings who are not notably deficient in mental functions, at least all such as psychologists have observed, possess a large stock of images and memories. The sight of a chair, for example, may call up in their minds a picture of the person who usually sits in it, or the sound of his name. The sound of a bell may call up the idea of

[1] Pp. 20 to 155 of this volume.
[2] *American Journal of Psychology*, Vol. X, pp. 256–279; Vol. XI, pp. 80–100, 131–165; Vol. XII, pp. 206–239.

dinner. The outside world also is to them in large part a multitude of definite percepts. They feel the environment as trees, sticks, stones, chairs, tables, letters, words, etc. I have called such definite presentations 'free ideas' to distinguish them from the vague presentations such as atmospheric pressure, the feeling of malaise, of the position of one's body when falling, etc. It is such 'free ideas' which compose the substance of thought and which lead us to perhaps the majority of the different acts we perform, though we do, of course, react to the vaguer sort as well. I saw definitely in writing the last sentence the words 'majority of the different acts' and thought 'we perform' and so wrote it. I see a bill and so take check book and pen and write. I think of the cold outside and so put on an overcoat. This mental function 'having free ideas,' gives the possibility of learning to meet situations properly by thinking about them, by being reminded of some property of the fact before us or some element therein.

We can divide all learning into (1) *learning by trial and accidental success*, by the strengthening of the connections between the sense-impressions representing the situation and the acts — or impulses and acts — representing our successful response to it and by the inhibition of similar connections with unsuccessful responses; (2) *learning by imitation*, where the mere performance by another of a certain act in a certain situation leads us to do the same; and (3) *learning by ideas*, where the situation calls up some idea (or ideas) which then arouses the act or in some way modifies it.

The last method of learning has obviously been the means of practically all the advances in civilization. The evidence quoted a paragraph or so back from the Experimental Study shows the typical mammalian mind to be one which rarely or never learns in this fashion. The present study of the primates has been a comparative study with two main questions in view: (1) How do the monkeys vary from the other mammals in the general mental functions revealed by their methods of learning? (2) How do they, on the other hand, vary from adult civilized human beings?

The experiments to be described seem, however, to be of value apart from the possibility of settling crucial questions by means of the evidence they give. To obtain exact accounts of what animals can learn by their own unaided efforts, by the example of their fellows or by the tuition of a trainer, and of how and how fast they learn in each case, seems highly desirable. I shall present the results in the manner which fits their consideration as arguments for or against some general hypotheses, but the naturalist or psychologist lacking the genetic interest may find an interest in them at their face value. I shall confine myself mainly to questions concerning the method of learning of the primates, and will discuss their sense-powers and un-learned reactions or instincts only in so far as is necessary to its comprehension.

It has been impossible for the author to make helpful use of the anecdotes and observations of naturalists and miscellaneous writers concerning monkey intelligence. The objections to such data pointed out in Chapter II, pp. 22–26, hold here. Moreover it is not practicable to sift out the true from the false or to interpret these random instances of animal behavior even if assuredly true. In the study of animal life the part is only clear in the light of the whole, and it is wiser to limit conclusions to such as are drawn from the constant and systematic study of a number of animals during a fairly long time. After a large enough body of such evidence has been accumulated we may be able to interpret random observations.

The subjects of the experiments were three South American monkeys of the genus *Cebus*. At the time of beginning the experiment No. 1 was about half grown, No. 2 was about one fourth full size and No. 3 was about half grown. No. 1 was under observation from November, 1899, to February, 1900; No. 2 and No. 3 from October, 1900, to February, 1901. No. 1 was during the period of experimentation decidedly tame, showing no fear whatever of my presence and little fear at being handled. He would handle and climb over me with no hesitation. No. 2 was timid, did not allow handling, but showed no fear of my presence and no phenomena that would differentiate his behavior in the experiments discussed from that of No. 1, save much greater caution in all respects. No. 3 also showed no fear at my presence. Any special individual traits that are of importance in connection with any of the observations will be mentioned in their proper places. No. 1 was kept until June, 1900, in my study in a cage 3 by 6 by 6 feet, and was left in the country till October, 1900. From October, 1900, all three were kept in a room 8 by 9 feet, in cages 6 feet tall by 3 long by 2.6 wide for Nos. 1 and 2, 3 feet by 3 feet by 20 inches for No. 3. I studied their behavior in learning to get into boxes, the doors to which could be opened by operating some mechanical contrivance, in learning to obtain food by other simple acts, in learning to discriminate between two signals, that is, to respond to each by a different act, and in their general life.

Following the order of the 'Animal Intelligence,' I shall first recount the observations of the way the monkeys learned, solely by their own unaided efforts, to operate simple mechanical contrivances.

Besides a number of boxes such as were used with the dogs and cats (see illustration on p. 30), I tried a variety of arrangements which could be set up beside a cage, and which would, when some simple mechanism was set in action, throw a bit of food into the cage. Figure 26 shows one of these. See description of QQ (ff) on page 182.

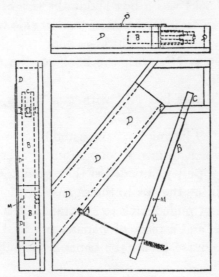

FIG. 26. *A*, loop; *BB*, lever, pivoted at *M*. A bit of food put in front of *C* would be thrown down the chute *DDD* when *A* was released.

APPARATUS

The different mechanisms which I used were the following: —

Box BB (O at back) was about 20 by 14 by 12 inches with a door in the front which was held by a bolt to which was tied a string. This string ran up the front of the box outside, over a pulley, across the top, and over another pulley down into the box, where it ended in a loop of wire.

Box MM (bolt) was the same as BB but with no string and loop attachment to the bolt.

Box CC (single bar) was a box of the same size as BB.

The door was held by a bar about 3 by 1 by 5 inches which swung on a nail at the left side.

Box CCC (double bar) was CC with a second similar bar on the right side of the door.

Box NN (hook) was a box about the size of BB with its door held by an ordinary hook on the left side which hooked through an eyelet screwed into the door.

Box NNN was NN with the hook on the right instead of the left side.

Box NNNN was box NN with two hooks, one on each side.

Apparatus OO (string box) consisted of a square box tied to a string, which formed a loop running over a pulley by the cage and a pulley outside, so that pulling on the under string would bring the box to the cage.   In each experiment the box was first pulled back to a distance of 2 feet 3 inches from the cage, and a piece of banana put in it.   The monkey could, of course, secure the banana by pulling the box near enough.

Apparatus OOO was the same as OO, with the box tied to the upper string, so that the upper string had to be pulled instead of the lower.

Box PP was about the size of BB.   Its door was held by a large string securely fastened at the right, passing across the front of the door and ending in a loop which was put over a nail on the box at the left of the door.   By pulling the string off the nail the door could be opened.

Box RR (wood plug) was a box about the size of BB. The door was held by a string at its top, which passed up over the front and top to the rear, where it was fastened to a wooden plug which was inserted in a hole in the top of the box.   When the plug was pulled out of the hole, the door would fall open.

Box SS (triple; wood-plug, hook and bar) was a box about the size of BB. To open the door, a bar had to be pushed around, a hook unhooked and a plug removed from a hole in the top of the box.

Box TT (nail plug) was 14 by 10 by 10 inches with a door 5.5 by 10 on the right side of the front, the rest of the front being barred up. The door was hinged at the bottom and fastened at its top to a wire which was fastened to a nail 2.5 inches long, which, when inserted in a hole 0.25 inches in diameter at the back of the top of the box, held the door closed. By drawing out this nail and pulling the door the animal could open the door.

Box VV (plug at side) was a box about 18 by 10 by 10, the door held by a plug passing through a hole in the side of the box. When the plug was pulled out, the door could be pushed inward.

Box W (loop) was 17 by 10 by 10 inches with a door 5 by 9 at the left side of its front hinged at the bottom. The door was prevented from falling inward by a wire stretched behind it. It was prevented from falling outward by a wire firmly fastened at the right side and held by a loop over a nail at the left. By pulling the loop outward and to the left it could be freed from the nail. The door could then be pulled open.

Box WW (bar inside) was 16 by 14 by 10 inches with a door 4 by 11 at the left of its front hinged at the bottom. The door could be pushed in or pulled out when a bar on its inside was lifted out of a latch. The bar was accessible from the outside through an opening in the front of the box. It had to be lifted to a height of 1.5 inches (an angle of about 30°).

Box XX (bar outside) was about 13 by 11 by 10 inches with a door 7 by 8 on the left side of the front. The door was held in place by a bar swinging on a nail at the top, with its other end resting in a latch at the left side of the box. By pushing this up through an angle of 45° the door could be opened.

Box YY (push bar) was a box 16 by 8 by 12 inches with a door at the left of its front. The door was held by a brass bar which swung down in front of an L-shaped piece of steel fastened to the inside of the door. This brass bar was hung on a pivot at its center and the other end attached to a bar of wood; the other end of this bar projected through a hole at the right side of the box. By pushing this bar in about an inch the door could be opened.

Box LL (triple; nail plug, hook and bar) was a box 10 by 10 by 13 with a door 3 by 8.5 at the left side. The door could be opened only after (1) a nail plug had been removed from a hole in the back of the top of the box as in TT, (2) a hook in the door had been unhooked, and (3) a bar on the left side had been turned from a horizontal to a vertical position.

Box Alpha (catch at back) was 11 by 10 by 15 with the door (4 by 4) in the left side of its front. The door was held by a bolt, which, when let down, held in a catch on the inside of the door. A string fastened to the bolt ran across to the back of the box and through a hole to the outside. There it ended in a piece of wood 2.5 by 1 by .25 inches. When this piece of wood was pulled, the bolt went up and the door fell open.

Box Beta was the same as NN except in size. It was 10 by 10 by 13 inches.

Box KK (triple; bolt, side plug, and knob) was a box 16 by 9 by 11 with a door at the left side of the front. The door was held by a bolt on the right side, a wooden plug stuck through a hole in the box on its left side and a nail which held in a catch at its top. This nail was fastened to a wooden knob (1 by 5 by .375) which lay in a depression at the top of the box. Only when the bolt had been drawn and the plug and knob pulled, could the door be opened.

Box Gamma (wind) was 10 by 10 by 13 inches with its door held by a wire fastened at the top and wound three times about a screw eye in the top of the box. By unwinding the wire the door could be opened.

Box Delta (push back) was 12 by 11 by 10 inches. Its door was held by a wooden bar projecting from the right two inches in front of it. This bar was so arranged that it could be pushed or pulled toward the right, allowing the door to fall open. It could not be swung up or down.

Box Epsilon (lever or push down) was 12 by 9 by 5 inches. At the right side of its front was a hole $\frac{1}{2}$ inch broad by $1\frac{1}{2}$ inches up and down. Across this hole on the inside of the box was a strip of brass, the end of one bar of a lever. If this strip was depressed $\frac{1}{8}$ of an inch, the door at the extreme left would be opened by a spring.

Box Zeta (side plug) was 12 by 11 by 10 inches. Its door was held by a round bar of wood put through a hoop of steel at the left side of the box. This bar was loose and could easily be pulled out, allowing the door to be opened.

Box Theta was the same as KK except that the door could be opened as soon as the bolt alone was pulled or pushed up.

Box Eta was like Alpha save that the object at the back of the box to be pulled was a brass ring.

Apparatus QQ (chute) consisted of a lever mechanism so arranged that by pushing in a bar of wood $\frac{1}{4}$ to $\frac{1}{2}$ an inch, a piece of banana would be thrown down a chute into the cage. The apparatus was placed outside the cage in such a way that it could be easily reached by the monkey's arm through the wire netting.

QQ (a) was of the same general plan. By turning a handle through 270° food could be obtained.

QQ (b) was like QQ (a) except that 2½ full revolutions of the handle in one direction were necessary to cause the food to drop down.

QQ (c) was a chute apparatus so arranged as to work when a nail was pulled out of a hole.

QQ (d) was arranged to work at a sharp pull upon a brass ring hanging to it.

QQ (e) was arranged to work when a hook was unhooked.

QQ (f) was arranged to work when a loop at the end of a string was pulled off from a nail.

QQ (ff) was QQ (f) with a stiff wire loop instead of a loop of string.

EXPERIMENTS ON THE ABILITIES OF THE MONKEYS TO LEARN WITHOUT TUITION

I will describe a few of the experiments with No. 1 as samples and then present the rest in the form of a table. No. 1 was tried first in BB (O at back) on January 17, 1900, being *put inside*. He opened the box by pulling up the string just above the bolt. His times were .05, 1.38, 6.00, 1.00, .10, .05, .05. He was not easily handled at this time, so I changed the experiment to the form adopted in future experiments. I put the food inside and left the animal to open the door from the outside. He pulled the string up within 10 seconds each time out of 10 trials.

I then tried him in MM (bolt). He failed in 15. I then (January 18th) tried him in CC (single bar outside.) He got in in 36.00 minutes; he did not succeed a second time that night, but in the morning the box was open. His times thenceforth were 20, 10, 16, 25 and on January 19th, 40, 5, 12, 8, 5, 5, 5 seconds.

I then tried him (January 21, 1900) in CCC (double bar). He did it at first by pushing the old bar and then pulling at the door until he worked the second bar gradually around. Later he at times pushed the second bar. The times taken are shown in the time-curve. I then (January 25th) tried him in NN (hook). See time-curves on page 185. I then (January 27th) tried him in NNN (hook on other side). He opened it in 6, 12 and 4 seconds in the first three trials. I then (20 minutes later) tried him with NNNN (double hook). He opened the door in 12, 10, 6 and 6 seconds. I then (January 27th) tried him with PP (string across). He failed in 10. I then (February 21st) tried him with apparatus OO (string box). For his progress as shown by the times taken see the time-curve. His progress is also shown in the decrease of the useless pullings at the wrong string. There were none in the 9th trial, 14th, 15th, 16th, 18th, 24th, and following trials.

No. 1 was then (February 24th) tried with OOO (string box with box on upper string). No. 1 succeeded in 2.20, then failed in 10.00. The rest of the experiment will be described under imitation.

He was next tried (March 24th) with apparatus QQ (chute). He failed in 10.00, though he played with the apparatus much of the time. Other experiments were with box RR (wood-plug) (April 5th). He failed in 10.00. After he had, in a manner to be described later, come to succeed with RR, he was tried in box SS (triple; wood-plug, hook and bar) (April 18th); see time-curve. No more experiments of this nature were tried until October, 1900.

The rest of the experiments with No. 1 and all those with

No. 2 and No. 3 may best be enumerated in the form of a table. (See Table 9 on page 187.) It will show briefly the range of performances which the unaided efforts of the animals can cope with. It will also give the order in which each animal experienced them. F means that the animal failed to succeed. The figures are minutes and seconds, and represent the time taken in the first trial or the total time taken without success where there is an F. In cases where the animal failed in say 10 minutes, but in a later trial succeeded, say in 2.40, the record will be 2.40 after 10 F. There are separate columns for all three animals, headed No. 1, No. 2 and No. 3. Im. stands for a practically immediate success.

The curves on pages 185 and 186 (Figs. 27 and 28) show the progress of the formation of the associations in those cases where the animal was given repeated trials, with, however, nothing to guide him but his own unaided efforts. Each millimeter on the abscissa represents one trial and each millimeter on the ordinate represents 10 seconds, the ordinates representing the time taken by the animal to open the box. A break in the curve, or an absence of the curve at the beginning of the base-line represents cases where the animal failed in 10 minutes or took a very long time to get out.

In discussing these facts we may first of all clear our way of one popular explanation, that this learning was due to 'reasoning.' If we use the word reasoning in its technical psychological meaning as the function of reaching conclusions by the perception of relations, comparison and inference, if we think of the mental content involved as feelings of relation, perceptions of similarity, general and abstract notions and judgments, we find no evidence of reasoning

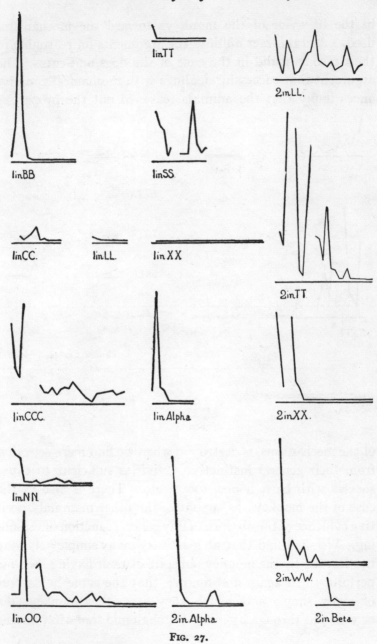

FIG. 27.

in the behavior of the monkeys toward the mechanisms
used.   And this fact nullifies the arguments for reasoning in
their case as it did in the case of the dogs and cats.   The
argument that successful dealings with mechanical contrivances imply that the animals reasoned out the properties

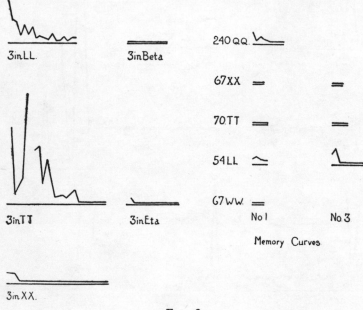

FIG. 28.

of the mechanisms, is destroyed when we find mere selection
from their general instinctive activities sufficient to cause
success with bars, hooks, loops, etc.   There is also in the
case of the monkeys, as in that of the other mammals, positive evidence of the absence of any general function of reasoning.   We shall find that at least very many simple acts were
not learned by the monkeys in spite of their having seen me
perform them again and again;   that the same holds true
of many simple acts which they saw other monkeys do,
or were put through by me.   We shall find that after having

TABLE 9

	No. 1			No. 2			No. 3		
	Date	Min. Sec.	F	Date	Min. Sec.	F	Date	Min. Sec.	F
Box TT (nail plug)	Oct. 19, 1900	0.40	F 60.00				Oct. 21, 1900	36.00	F 10.00
Box UU (old plug at side)	Oct. 19, 1900		F 10.00				Oct. 22, 1900		F 10.00
Box VV (wire loop)	Oct. 20, 1900		F 10.00	Oct. 21, 1900	14.10	F 10.00	Oct. 22, 1900		F 10.00
Box WW (bar inside)	Oct. 20, 1900	im.	F 10.00	Oct. 24, 1900 / Oct. 25, 1900	5.00	F 10.00 / F 10.00	Oct. 24, 1900		{ F 5.00 / F 10.00 / F 15.00 }
Box XX (bar outside)	Oct. 23, 1900	im.	after[1] / F 10.00	Oct. 21, 1900	3.40	after / F 30.00	Oct. 23, 1900	.30	F 10.00
Box YY (push bar)	Oct. 30, 1900	2.00[2]	F 10.00	Oct. 24, 1900	9.00	after / F 10.00 and 10.00	Oct. 24, 1900	im.	F 10.00
Box Beta (single hook)				Oct. 30, 1900					
Box LL (triple; nail plug, hook and bar outside)	Nov. 4, 1900	16.00[3]	F 10.00	Oct. 3, 1900	2.00		Nov. 3, 1900	1.45	F 10.00
Box Alpha (catch at back)	Nov. 5, 1900	.35	F 10.00	Oct. 5, 1900	6.00	F 60.00	Nov. 5, 1900		F 10.00
Box KK (triple; bolt, side-plug and kno.)	Nov. 7, 1900		F 10.00	Oct. 7, 1900			Nov. 7, 1900		F 60.00
Box Theta (bolt at top)	Nov. 19, 1900	im.					Jan. 8, 1901		F 10.00
Box Eta (ring at back)	Dec. 17, 1900	.20					Dec. 17, 1900	4.20	F 60.00
App. QQ (push chute)	Jan. 3, 1901						Dec. 17, 1900		F 10.00
Box Gamma (wind)	Jan. 4, 1901		F 5.00				Jan. 4, 1900		F 10.00
Box Delta (push back)	Jan. 4, 1901	.20	F 5.00				Jan. 4, 1901	2.10	after[4] / F 10.00
App. QQ (a) (bar chute)	Jan. 6, 1901	8.00	after				Jan. 7, 1901		F 10.00
Box Zeta (new side plug)	Jan. 7, 1901	1.10	F 5.00				Jan. 8, 1901	.50	F 10.00
App. QQ (b) (2¼ revolution chute)	Jan. 9, 1901	3.00	F 5.00				Jan. 8, 1901		F 10.00
App. QQ (c) (nail-plug chute)	Jan. 11, 1901		F 5.00				Jan. 11, 1901		F 5.00
Box Epsilon (push down)	Jan. 12, 1901		F 10.00				Jan. 12, 1901		F 5.00
App. QQ (d) (ring chute)	Jan. 16, 1901		F 5.00				Jan. 16, 1901	im.	F 10.00
App. QQ (e) (hook chute)			F 5.00				Jan. 16, 1901		F 5.00
App. QQ (f) (string chute)	Jan. 17, 1901		F 5.00				Jan. 19, 1901		F 5.00
App. QQ (ff) (string-wire chute)	Jan. 17, 1901	.20	F 5.00						

[1] Practically a memory trial of CC, done January 21, 1900.
[2] Did it by pulling door and thus shaking lever.
[3] Practically a memory trial of SS.
[4] Did it by pulling door and biting wire.

abundant opportunity to realize that one signal meant food at the bottom of the cage and another none, a monkey would not act from the obvious inference and consistently stay up or go down as the case might be, but would make errors such as would be natural if he acted under the growing influence of an association between sense-impression and impulse or sense-impression and idea, but quite incomprehensible if he had compared the two signals and made a definite inference. We shall find that, after experience with several pairs of signals, the monkeys yet failed, when a new pair was used, to do the obvious thing to a rational mind; viz., to compare the two, think which meant food, and act on the knowledge directly.

The methods one has to take to get them to do anything, their general conduct in becoming tame and in the experiments throughout, confirm these conclusions. The following particular phenomena are samples of the many which are inconsistent with the presence of reasoning as a general function. No. 1 had learned to open a door by pushing a bar around from a horizontal to a vertical position. The same box was then fitted with two bars. He turned the first bar round thirteen times before attempting to push the other bar around. In box LL all three monkeys would in the early trials do one or two of the acts over and over after they had once done them. No. 1, who had learned to pull a loop of wire off from a nail, failed thereafter to pull off a similar loop made of string. No. 1 and No. 3 had learned to poke their left hands through the cage for me to take and operate a chute with. It was extremely difficult to get either of them to put his right hand through or even to let me take it and pull it through.

A negative answer to the question "Do the monkeys reason?" thus seems inevitable, but I do not attach to the question an importance commensurate with the part it has played historically in animal psychology. For I think it can be shown, and I hope in a later monograph to show, that reasoning is probably but one secondary result of the general function of having free ideas in great numbers, one product of a type of brain which works in great detail, not in gross associations. The denial of reasoning need not mean, and does not to my mind, any denial of continuity between animal and human mentality or any denial that the monkeys are mentally nearer relatives to man than are the other mammals.

So much for supererogatory explanation. Let us now turn to a more definite and fruitful treatment of these records.

The difference between these records and those of the chicks, cats and dogs given on pages 39–65 *passim* is undeniable. Whereas the latter were practically unanimous, save in the cases of the very easiest performances, in showing a process of gradual learning by a gradual elimination of unsuccessful movements, and a gradual reënforcement of the successful one, these are unanimous, save in the very hardest, in showing a process of sudden acquisition by a rapid, often apparently instantaneous, abandonment of the unsuccessful movements and a selection of the appropriate one which rivals in suddenness the selections made by human beings in similar performances. It is natural to infer that the monkeys who suddenly replace much general pulling and clawing by a single definite pull at a hook or bar have an idea of the hook or bar and of the movement they make. The rate of their progress is so different from that of the cats and dogs that we cannot help imagining as the cause of it a totally different mental function, namely, free ideas instead of vague sense-impressions and impulses.   But our interpretation of these results should not be too hasty.   We must first consider several other possible explanations of the rapidity of learning by the monkeys before jumping to the conclusion that the forces which bring about the sudden formation of associations in human beings are present.

First of all it might be that the difference was due to the superiority of the monkeys in clear detailed vision.   It might be that in given situations where associations were to be formed on the basis of smells, the cats and dogs would show similar rapid learning.   There might be, that is, no general difference in type of mental functioning, but only a special difference in the field in which the function worked.   This question can be answered by an investigation of the process of forming associations in connection with smells by dogs and cats.   Such an investigation will, I hope, soon be carried on in the Columbia Laboratory by Mr. Davis.[1]

Secondly, it might be that the superior mobility and more detailed and definite movements of the monkeys' hands might have caused the difference.   The slowness in the case of the dogs and cats might be at least in part the result of difficulty in executing movements, not in intending them. This difficulty in execution is a matter that cannot be readily estimated, but the movements made by the cats and dogs would not on their face value seem to be hard.   They were mostly common to the animals' ordinary life.   At the same time there were certain movements (*e.g.* depressing the lever) which were much more quickly associated with their respective situations by the cats than others were, and if we could suppose that all the movements learned by the monkeys were comparable to these few, it would detract

[1] This, I regret, was not done [E. L. T., 1911].

from the necessity of seeking some general mental difference as the explanation of the difference in the results.

In the third place it may be said by some that no comparison of the monkeys with dogs and cats is valid, since the former animals got out of boxes while the latter got in. It may be supposed that the instinctive response to confinement includes an agitation which precludes anything save vague unregulated behavior. Professor Wesley Mills has made such a suggestion in referring to the 'Animal Intelligence' in the *Psychological Review*, May, 1899. In the July number of the same journal I tried to show that there was no solid evidence of such a harmful agitation. Nor can we be at all sure that agitation when present does not rather quicken the wits of animals. It often seems to. However I should, of course, allow that for purposes of comparison it would be better to have the circumstances identical. And I should welcome any antagonist who should, by making experiments with kittens after the fashion of these with the monkeys, show that they did learn as suddenly as the latter.

Again we know that, whereas the times taken by a cat in a box to get out are inversely proportional to the strength of the association, inasmuch as they represent fairly the amount of its efforts, on the other hand, the times taken by a monkey to get in represent the amounts of his efforts *plus the amount of time in which he is not trying to get in*. It may be said therefore that the time records of the monkeys prove nothing,—that a record of four minutes may mean thirty seconds of effort and three minutes thirty seconds of sleep,— that one minute may really represent twice as much effort. As a matter of fact this objection would occasionally hold against some single record. The earliest times and the occasional long times amongst very short ones are likely to be too long. The first fact makes the curves have too great a drop at the start, making them seem cases of too sudden learning, but the second fact makes the learning seem indefinite when it really is not. And in the long run the times taken do represent fairly well the amount of effort. I carefully recorded the amount of actual effort in a number of cases and the story it tells concerning the mental processes involved is the same as that told by the time-curves.

Still another explanation is this: The monkeys learn quickly, it is true, but not quickly enough for us to suppose the presence of ideas, or the formation of associations among them. For if there were such ideas, they should in the complex acts do even better than they did. The explanation then is a high degree of facility in the formation of associations of just the same kind as we found in the chicks, dogs and cats.

Such an explanation we could hardly disapprove in any case. No one can from objective evidence set up a standard of speed of learning below which all shall be learning without ideas and above which all shall be learning by ideas. We should not expect any hard and fast demarcation.

This whole matter of the rate of learning should be studied in the light of other facts of behavior. My own judgment, if I had nothing but these time-curves to rely on, would be that there was in them an appearance of learning by ideas which, while possibly explicable by the finer vision and freer movements of the monkey in connection with ordinary mammalian mentality, made it worth while to look farther into their behavior. This we may now do.

What leads the lay mind to attribute superior mental gifts to an animal is not so much the rate of learning as the amount learned. The monkeys obviously form more associations and associations in a greater variety than do the other mammals. The improved rate assists, but another cause of this greater number of associations is the general physical activity of the monkeys, their constant movements of the hands, their instinctive curiosity or tendency to fool with all sorts of objects, to enjoy having sense-impressions, to form associations because of the resulting sound or sight. These mental characteristics are of a high degree of importance from the comparative point of view, but they cannot be used to prove that the monkeys have free ideas, for a large number of associations may be acquired after the purely animal fashion.

What is of more importance is the actual behavior of the animals in connection with the boxes. First of all, as has been stated, all the monkey's movements are more definite, he seems not merely to pull, but to pull at, not merely to poke, but to push at. He seems, even in his general random play, to go here and there, pick up this, examine the other, etc., more from having the idea strike him than from feeling like doing it. He seems more like a man at the breakfast table than like a man in a fight. Still this appearance may be quite specious, and I think it is likely to lead us to read ideational life into his behavior if we are not cautious. It may be simply general activity of the same sort as the narrower activities of the cat or dog.

In the second place the monkeys often make special movements with a directness which reminds one unavoidably of human actions guided by ideas. For instance, No. 1 escaped from his cage one day and went directly across the room to a table where lay a half of a banana which was in a very inconspicuous place. It seemed as if he had observed the banana and acted with the idea of its position fully in mind. Again, on failing to pull a hook out, No. 1 immediately applied his teeth, though he had before always pulled it out with his hand. So again with a plug. It may be that there is a special inborn tendency to bite at objects pulled unsuccessfully. If not, the act would seem to show the presence of the idea 'get thing out' or 'thing come out' and associated with it the impulse to use the teeth. We shall see later, however, that in certain other circumstances where we should expect ideas to be present and result in acts they do not.

The fact is that those features in the behavior of the monkeys in forming associations between the sight of a box and the act needed to open it which remind us of learning by ideas may also be possibly explained by general activity and curiosity, the free use of the hand, and superior quickness in forming associations of the animal sort. We must have recourse to more crucial tests or at least seek evidence from a number of different kinds of mental performances. The first of these will naturally be their behavior toward these same mechanisms after a long time-interval.

The Permanence of Associations in the Case of Mechanisms

My records are too few and in all but one case after too short an interval to be decisive on the point of abrupt transition from failure to success such as would characterize an animal in whose mind arose the idea of a certain part of the mechanism as the thing to be attacked or of a certain movement as the fit one. The animals are all under observation in the Columbia Laboratory, however, and I trust that later satisfactory tests may be made. No. 2 was not included in the tests because he was either unwell or had become very shy of the boxes, entering them even when the door was left open only after great delay.   The time-curves for the experiments performed will be found on page 186 among the others.   The figures beside each pair represent the number of days without practice.

The records show a decided superiority to those of the cats and dogs.   Although the number of trials in the original tests were in general fewer in the case of the monkeys, the retention of the association is complete in 6 cases out of 8 and is practically so in one case where the interval was 8 months.

EXPERIMENTS ON THE DISCRIMINATION OF SIGNALS

My experiments on discrimination were of the following general type: I got the animal into the habit of reacting to a certain signal (a sound, movement, posture, visual presentation or what not) by some well-defined act.   In the cases to be described this act was to come down from his customary positions about the top of the cage, to a place at the bottom.   I then would give him a bit of food.   When this habit was wholly or partly formed, I would begin to mix with that signal another signal enough like it so that the animal would respond in the same manner.   In the cases where I gave this signal I would not feed him.   I could then determine whether the animal did discriminate or not, and his progress toward perfect discrimination in case he did. If an animal responds indiscriminately to both signals (that is, does not learn to disregard the 'no food' signal) it is well to test him by using two somewhat similar signals, after one of which you feed him at one place and after the other of which you feed him at a different place.

If the animal profits by his training by acquiring ideas of

the two signals and associates with them ideas of 'food' and 'no food,' 'go down' and 'stay still,' and uses these ideas to control his conduct, he will, we have a right to expect, change suddenly from total failure to differentiate the signals to total success. He will or won't have the ideas, and will behave accordingly. The same result could, of course, be brought about by very rapid association of the new signal with the act of keeping still, a very rapid inhibition of the act of going down in response to it by virtue of the lack of any pleasure from doing so.

For convenience I shall call the signals after which food was given *yes* signals and those after which food was not given *no* signals. Signals not described in the text are shown in Fig. 29, below. The progress of the monkeys in

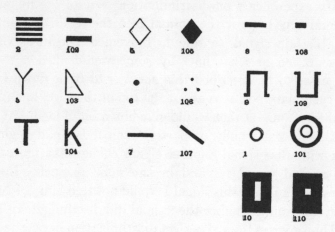

FIG. 29.

discriminating is shown by Figs. 30 and 31, on pages 199 and 201. In Figs. 30 and 31 every millimeter along the horizontal or base line represents 10 trials with the signal. The heights of the black surface represent the percentages of *wrong* responses, 10 mm. meaning 100 per cent of incorrect responses. Thus the first figure of the set, Left hand, *a*, presents the following record: First 10 trials, all wrong; of next 10, 7 wrong; of next 10, 6 wrong; of next 10, 7; of the next, 9; of the next, 9; of the next, 4; of the next, none; of the next, 3; of the next, 2, and then 70 trials without an error.

I will describe some of the experiments in detail and then discuss the graphic presentation of them all.

EXPERIMENTS WITH NO. 1

Having developed in No. 1 the habit of coming down to the bottom of his cage to get a bit of food when he saw me reach out and take such a bit from my desk, I tested his ability to discriminate by beginning to use now one hand, now the other, feeding him only when I used the left. I also used different sets of words, namely, 'I will give some food' and 'They shall not have any.' It will be seen later that he probably reacted only to the difference of the hands. The experiment is similar to that described on pages 129 and 130 of Chapter II. At the beginning, it should be remembered, No. 1 would come down whichever hand was used, no matter what was said, except in the occasional cases where he was so occupied with some other pursuit as to be evidently inattentive. He did come to associate the act of going down with the one signal and the act of staying still or continuing his ordinary movements with the other signal. His progress in learning to do so is best seen in the curves of his errors. To the 'yes' signal he responded correctly, except for the occasional lapses which I just mentioned, from the start and throughout. With the 'no' signal his errors were as shown in Fig. 30, *a*. The break in the curve at 110 and 120 is probably not significant of an actual retrograde as the trials concerned followed an eight days' cessation of the experiments.

I next tried No. 1 with an apparatus exposing sometimes a card with a diamond-shaped piece of buff-colored paper on it and sometimes a card with a similar black piece. The black piece was three fourths of an inch farther behind the opening than the other. The light color was the 'yes' signal. The error curves for both signals are given, as No. 1 at the beginning of the experiment did not go down always (Fig. 30, b and b_1).

I next tried No. 1 with the same apparatus but exposing cards with YES and N in place of the buff and black diamonds. The record of the errors is given in Fig. 30, c and c_1. At the start he came down halfway very often. This I arbitrarily scored as an error no matter which signal it was in response to. It should not be supposed that these curves represent two totally new associations. It seems likely that the monkey reacted to the *position* of the N card in the apparatus (the same as that of the black diamond card) rather than to the shape of the letters. On putting the black diamond in front he was much confused.

I next gave No. 1 the chance to form the habits of coming down when I rapped my pencil against the table twice and of staying where he was when I rapped with it once. He had 90 trials of each signal but failed to give evidence of any different associations in the two cases.

Experiments of this sort were discontinued in the summer. In October I tried No. 1 with the right and left hand experiment, he being in a new room and cage, and I being seated in a different situation. He came down at both signals and failed to make any ascertainable progress with the no signal in 80 trials. (October 20–24.)

I then tried him with the black and buff diamonds, the

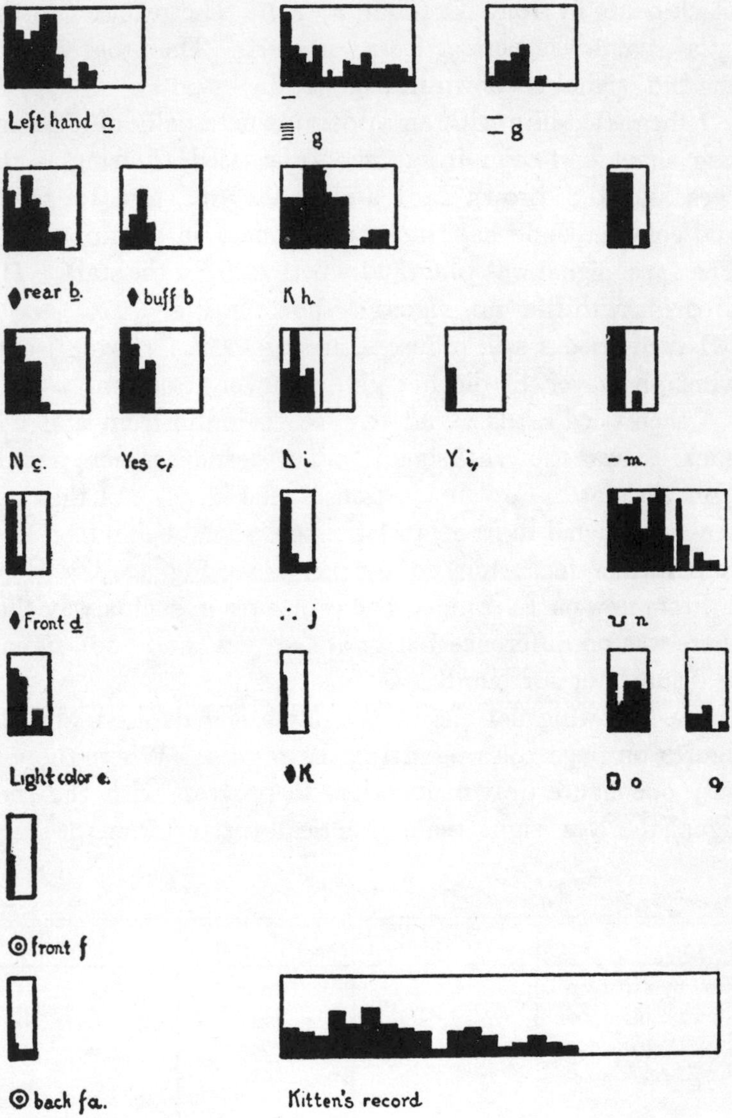
Left hand a
g
g
rear b.
buff b
K h.
N c.
Yes c,
i
Y i,
- m.
Front d
j
n
Light color e.
K
o
q
front f
back fa.
Kitten's record

FIG. 30.

black being in front (October 25–29). The reaction to the 'yes' signal was perfect from the start. The progress with the 'no' signal is shown in Fig. 30, *d*.

I then tried him with an apparatus externally of different size, shape and color from that so far used, showing as the 'yes' signal a brown card and as the 'no' signal a white and gold card one half inch farther back in the apparatus. The 'yes' signal was practically perfect from the start. His progress with the 'no' signal is shown in Fig. 30, *e*.

I then tried a still different arrangement for exposure, to which, however, he did not give uniform attention.

I then tried cards 1 and 101, 101 being in front and 1 in back. 1 was the 'yes' signal. 'Yes' responses were perfect from the start. For 'no' responses see Fig. 30, *f*. I then put the 'yes' signal in front and the 'no' signal behind. 'Yes' responses perfect; for 'no' responses see Fig. 30, *f*, *a*.

From now on I arranged the exposures in such a way that there was no difference between the 'yes' and 'no' signals in distance or surroundings.

The following list shows the dates, signals used, and the figures on page 199 presenting the results. Where there is only one figure drawn, it refers to progress with the 'no' signal, the 'yes' signal being practically perfect from the start.

TABLE 10

	'YES' SIGNAL	'NO' SIGNAL	FIGURE
Nov. 13–15, 1900.	2	102	*g* *g₁*
Nov. 14–16, 1900.	3	103	*i* *i₁*
Nov. 16–19, 1900.	4	104	*h*
Nov. 19, 1900.	5	105	*j*
Nov. 20, 1900.	6	106	*k*
Nov. 21, 1900.	7	107	*l*
Nov. 23(?) 1900.	8	108	*m*
Nov. 27–29, 1900.	9	109	*n*
Nov. 30, 1900.	10	110	*o*

Fig. 29 gives facsimiles of the different signals reduced to one sixth their actual size. The drawing of 101 is not accurate, the outer ring being too thick.

EXPERIMENTS WITH NO. 2

I first secured the partial formation of the habit of coming down when I took a bit of food in my hand. I then used the apparatus for exposing cards, YES in front being the 'yes' signal and a circle at the back being the 'no' signal. I gave No. 2 25 trials with the 'yes' signal and then began a regular

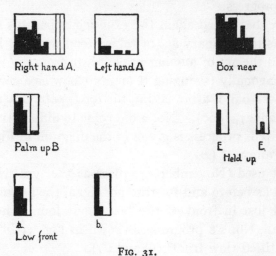

Right hand A.   Left hand A   Box near

Palm up B   E   E
                            Held up

a.   b.
Low front

FIG. 31.

experiment similar to those described. After about 90 trials (November 9–12, 1900) there was no progress toward differentiation of response, and it was evident from No. 2's behavior that he was reacting solely to the movements of my hand. So I abandoned the exposing apparatus and used (November 11–13, 1900) as the 'yes' signal the act of taking the food with my left hand from a pile on the front of the box and for the 'no' signal the act of taking food with my right hand from a pile 4 inches behind that just mentioned.

No. 2 did come to differentiate these two signals. The record of his progress is given in Fig. 31 by A and A_1.

I then made a second attempt with the exposing apparatus, using cards 2 and 102 (November 6, 14–21). No. 2 did react to my movements in pulling the string but in over 100 trials made no progress in the direction of a differential reaction to the 'no' signal. I then tried feeding him at each signal, feeding him at the bottom of the cage as usual when I gave the 'yes' signal and at the top when I gave the 'no' signal. After a hundred trials with the 'no' signal there was no progress.

I then abandoned again the exposing apparatus and used as signals the ordinary act of taking food with my left hand (yes) and the act of moving my left arm from my right side round diagonally (swinging it on my elbow as a center) and holding the hand, after taking the food, *palm up* (no) (November 26, 27, 1900). No. 2 did come to differentiate these signals. His progress is given in the diagram in Fig. 31 entitled 'Palm up' (B).

I next used (November 27, 1900) as the 'yes' signal the same act as before and for the 'no' signal the act of holding the food just in front of the box about four inches below the edge. No. 2's progress is shown in Fig. 31 in the diagram entitled 'low front' (C and C_1).

I next used (November 27–30) the same movement for both 'yes' and 'no' signals save that as the 'yes' signal I took the food from a brown pasteboard box 3 by 3 by 0.5, and as the 'no' signal I took it from a white crockery cover two inches in diameter and three eighths of an inch high which was beside the box but three inches nearer me. No. 2's progress is shown in Fig. 31 in the diagram entitled 'Box near' (D).

I next used for the 'yes' signal the familiar act and for the 'no' signal the act of holding the food six inches above the box instead of a quarter or a half an inch. The progress is shown in Fig. 31, E and E_1. I then tried taking the food from a saucer off the front of the box for the 'yes' signal and from a small box at the back for the 'no' signal. 'Yes' was perfect from the start (10 trials given). 'No' was right once, then wrong once, then right for the remaining eight.

EXPERIMENTS WITH NO. 3

No. 3 was kept in a cage not half so big as those of 1 and 2. Perhaps because of the hindrance this fact offered to forming the habit of reacting in some definite way to 'yes' signals, perhaps because of the fact that I did not try hand movements as signals, there was no successful discrimination by No. 3 of the yellow from the black diamond or of a card with YES from a card with a circle on it. I tried climbing up to a particular spot as the response to the 'yes' signal and staying still as the response to the 'no' signal. I also tried instead of the latter a different act, in which case the animal was fed after both signals but in different places. In the latter case No. 3 made some progress, but for practical reasons I postponed experiments with him. Circumstances have made it necessary to postpone such experiments indefinitely.

PERMANENCE OF THE ABILITY TO DISCRIMINATE

No. 1 and No. 2 were tried again after intervals of 33 to 48 days. The results of these trials are shown in Fig. 32. Here every millimeter along the base line represents *one* trial with the 'no' signal (the 'yes' signals were practically perfect), and failure is represented by a column 10 n.m. high while

success is represented by the absence of any column.　Thus
the first record reads, "No. 1 with signal 104 after 40 days
made 5 failures, then 2
successes, then 1 fail-
ure, then 1 success,
then 3 failures, then 1
success, then 1 failure,
then 3 successes, then
1 failure, then 10 suc-
cesses."　The third
record (106; 40 days)
reads, "perfect success
in ten trials."

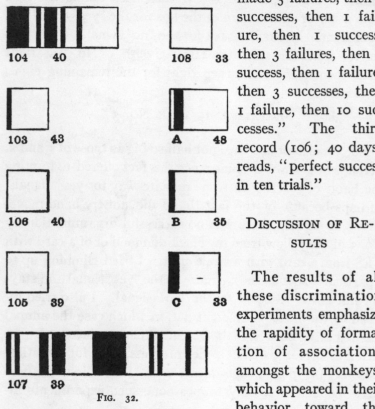

FIG. 32.

DISCUSSION OF RE-
SULTS

The results of all
these discrimination
experiments emphasize
the rapidity of forma-
tion of associations
amongst the monkeys,
which appeared in their
behavior toward the
mechanisms.　The suddenness of the change in many cases
is immediately suggestive of human performances.　If all
the records were like c, f, h, i, j, k, l, m, B, E, and memory
trials 103, A, B, and C, one would have to credit the animals
with either marvelous rapidity in forming associations of
the purely animal sort or concede that from all the objective
evidence at hand they were shown to learn as human beings
would.　One would have to suppose that they had clear

ideas of the signals and clean-cut associations with those ideas. The other records check such a conclusion.

In studying the figures we should remember that occasional mistakes, say 1 in 10 trials, are probably not significant of incomplete learning but of inattention or of precipitate action before the shutter had fairly exposed the card. We must not expect that a monkey who totally fails to discriminate will *always* respond wrongly to the 'no' signal, or that a monkey who has come to discriminate perfectly will *always* respond rightly. A sudden drop from an average high level of error to an average low level will signify sudden learning. Where the failure was on the first trial of a series a few hours or a day removed from the last series, I have generally represented the fact not by a column 1 mm. high and 1 mm. broad, but by a single 10 mm. perpendicular. See i and A. Such cases represent probably the failure of the animal to keep his learning permanent rather than any general inability to discriminate.

K was to some extent a memory trial of d (after over half a year).

The experiment with 10 and 110 is noteworthy. Although, as can be seen from the figures, the difference is obvious to one looking at the white part of the figure, it is not so to one looking at the black part. No. 1 failed to improve appreciably in fifty trials, probably because his previous experience had gotten him into the habit of attending to the black lines.

Before arguing from the suddenness of the change from failure to success we have to consider one possibility that I have not mentioned, and in fact for the sake of clearness in presentation have rather concealed. It is that the sudden change in the records, which report only whether the animal did or did not go down, may represent a more gradual change in the animal's mind, a gradual weakening of the impulse to go down which makes him feel less and less inclined to go down, though still doing so, until this weakening reaches a sort of saturation point and stops the action. There were in their behavior some phenomena which might witness to such a process, but their interpretation is so dependent on the subjective attitude and prepossessions of the observer that I prefer not to draw any conclusions from them. On the other hand, records c, g, n, A and D seem to show that gradual changes can be paralleled by changes in the percentage of failures.

In the statement of conclusions I shall represent what would be the effect on our theory of the matter in both cases, (1) taking the records to be fairly perfect parallels of the process, and (2) taking them to be the records of the summation points of a process not shown with surety in any measurable objective facts. But I shall leave to future workers the task of determining which case is the true one.

If we judge by the objective records themselves, we may still choose between two views. (1) We may say that the monkeys did come to have ideas of the acts of going down to the bottom of the cage and of staying still, and that their learning represented the association of the sense-impressions of the two signals, one with each of these ideas, or possibly their association with two other ideas (of being fed and of not being fed), and through them with the acts. Or (2) we may say that the monkeys had no such ideas, but merely by the common animal sort of association came to react in the profitable way to each signal.

If we take the first view, we must explain the failure of the animals to change suddenly in some of the experiments, must explain why, for instance, No. 1 in g should, after he had responded correctly to the 'no' signal for 27 trials out of 30,

fail in one trial out of four for a hundred or more trials. If
the 27 successes were due to ideas, why was there regression?
If the animal came to respond by staying still on seeing the
K (card 104), because that sight was associated with the idea
of no food or the idea of staying still, why did he, in his
memory trial, act sometimes rightly, sometimes wrongly, for
eleven trials after his acting rightly twice. If he stayed still
because the idea was aroused, why did he not stay still as
soon as he had a few trials to remind him of the idea? It is
easy, one may say, to see why, with a capacity to select
movements and associate them with sense-presentations
very quickly, in cases where habit provides only two movements for selection and where the sense-presentation is very
clear and simple, an animal should practically at once be
confirmed in the one act on an occasion when he does it
with the sense-impression in the focus of attention. It is
easy, therefore, to explain the sudden change in i, l, m, B, C
and E. But our critic may add, "It is very hard to suppose
that an animal that learned by connecting the sight of a card
with the idea 'stay still' or the idea 'no food,' should be so
long in making the connection as was the case in some of
these experiments, should take 10, 20 or 40 trials to change
from a high percentage of wrong to a high percentage of
right reactions."

If we take the second view, we have to face the fact that
many of the records are nothing like the single one we have
for comparison, that of the kitten shown in Fig. 30, and that
the appeal to a capacity to form animal associations very
quickly seems like a far-fetched refuge from the other view
rather than a natural interpretation. If we take the records to be summation points in a more gradual process, this
difficulty is relieved.

If further investigation upheld the first view, we should

still not have a demonstration that the monkeys habitually did learn by getting percepts and images associated with sense-impressions, by having free ideas of the acts they performed; we should only have proved that they could under certain circumstances.

The circumstances in these experiments on discrimination were such as to form a most favorable case. The act of going down had been performed in all sorts of different connections and was likely to gain representation in ideational life; the experience 'bit of banana' had again been attended to as a part of very many different associations and so would be likely to develop into a definite idea.

These results then do not settle the choice between three theories: (1 *a*) that they were due to a general capacity for having ideas, (1 *b*) that they were due to ideas acquired by specially favoring circumstances, (2) that they were due to the common form of association, the association of an impulse to an act with a sense-impression rather roughly felt.

It would be of the utmost interest to duplicate these experiments with dogs, cats and other mammals and compare the records. Moreover, since we shall find (1 *a*) barred out by other experiments, it will be of great interest to test the monkeys with some other type of act than discrimination to see if, by giving the animal experience of the act and result involved in many different connections, we can get a rate of speed in the formation of a new association comparable to the rates in some of these cases.

Of course here, as in our previous section, the differences in the sense-powers of the monkeys from those of the kitten which I have tested with a similar experiment may have caused the difference in behavior. Focalized vision lends itself to delicate associations. Perhaps if one used the sense of smell, or if the dogs and cats could, preserving their same mental faculties in general, add the capacity for focalized vision, they would do as well as the monkeys.

EXPERIMENTS ON THE INFLUENCE OF TUITION

The general aim of these experiments was to ascertain whether the monkeys' actions were at all determined by the presence of free ideas and if so, to what extent. The question is, "Are the associations which experience leads them to form, associations between (1) the idea of an object and (2) the idea of an act or result and (3) the impulses and act itself, or are they merely associations between the sense-impression of the object and the impulse and act?" Can a monkey learn and does he commonly learn to do things, not by the mere selection of the act from amongst the acts done by him, but by getting some idea and then himself providing the act because it is associated in his mind with that idea. If a monkey feels an impulse to get into a box, sees his arm push a bar and sees a door fall open immediately thereafter and goes into the box enough times, he has every chance to form the association between the impulse to get into the box and the idea 'arm push bar,' provided he can have such an idea. If his general behavior is due to having ideas connected with and so causing his acts, he has had chance enough to form the association between the idea 'push at' and the act of pushing. If then a monkey forms an association leading to an act by being put through the act, we may expect that he has free ideas. And if he has free ideas in general in connection with his actions, we may expect him to so form associations. So also if a monkey shows a general capability to learn from seeing another monkey or a human being do a thing. A few isolated cases of imitation, however, might witness not to any general mental quality, but only to certain instincts or habits differing from others only in that the situation calling forth the act was the same act performed by another.

If the monkeys do not learn in these ways, we must, until other evidence appears, suppose them to be in general destitute of a life of free ideas, must regard their somewhat ambiguous behavior in learning by their own unaided efforts as of the same type as that of the dogs and cats, differing only in the respects mentioned on pages 190 and 191.

The general method of experimentation was to give monkeys who had failed of their own efforts to operate some simple mechanism, a chance to see me do it or see another monkey do it or to see and feel themselves do it, and then note any change in their behavior. The chief question is whether they succeed after such tuition when they have failed before it, but the presence of ideas would also be indicated if they attacked, though without success, the vital point in the mechanism when they had not done so before. On the other hand, mere success would not prove that the tuition had influenced them, for if they made a different movement or attacked a different spot, we could not attribute their behavior to getting ideas of the necessary act.

The results of the experiments as a whole are on their face value a trifle ambiguous, but they surely show that the monkeys in question had no considerable stock of ideas of the objects they dealt with or of the movements they made and were not in general capable of acquiring, from seeing me or one of their comrades attack a certain part of a mechanism and make a certain movement, any ideas that were at all efficacious in guiding their conduct. They do not acquire or use ideas in anything that approaches the way human adults do. Whether the monkeys may not have some few ideas corresponding to habitual classes of objects and acts is a different question. Such may be present and function as the excitants of acts.

It is likely that this question could have been definitely solved if it had been possible for me to work with a larger number of animals. With enough subjects one could use the method mentioned on page 105 of Chapter II, of giving the animals tuition in acts which they would eventually do themselves without it, and then leaving them to their efforts, noting any differences in the way they learned from that in which other subjects who had no tuition learned the same acts. The chief of such differences to note would be differences in the time of their first trial, in the slope of the time-curve and in the number of useless acts.

It would also be possible to extend experiments of the type of the (on chair) experiment, where a subject is given first a certain time (calculated by the experimenter to be somewhat less than would be needed for the animal to hit upon the act) and if he does fail is then given certain tuition and then a second trial. The influence of the tuition is estimated by the presence or absence of cases where after tuition the act is done within the time.

There is nothing necessarily insoluble in the problem. Given ten or twenty monkeys that can be handled without any difficulty and it could be settled in a month.

With this general preface we may turn to the more special questions connected with the experiments on imitation of human acts and of the acts of other monkeys and on the formation of associations apart from the selection of impulses.

IMITATION OF HUMAN BEINGS

It has been a common opinion that monkeys learned to do things from seeing them done by human beings.

We find anecdotes to that effect in fairly reputable authors.

Of course, such anecdotes might be true and still not prove that the animals learned to do things because they saw them done. The animal may have been taught in other ways to respond to the particular sights in question by the particular acts. Or it may have been in each case a coincidence.

If a monkey did actually form an association between a given situation and act by seeing some one respond to that situation by that act, it would be evidence of considerable importance concerning his general mental status, for it would go to show that he could and often did form associations between sense-impressions and ideas and between ideas and acts. Seeing some one turn a key in a lock might thus give him the idea of turning or moving the key, and this idea might arouse the act. However, the mere fact that a monkey does something which you have just done in his presence need not demonstrate or even render a bit more probable such a general mental condition. For he perhaps would have acted in just the same manner if you had offered him no model. If you put two toothpicks on a dish, take one and put it in your mouth, a monkey will do the same, not because he profits by your example, but because he instinctively puts nearly all small objects in his mouth. Because of their general activity, their instinctive impulses to grab, drop, bite, rub, carry, move about, turn over, etc., any novel object within their reach, their constant movement and assumption of all sorts of postures, the monkeys perform many acts like our own and simulate imitation to a far greater extent than other mammals.

Even if a monkey which has failed of itself to do a certain thing does it after you have shown him the act, there need be no reason to suppose that he is learning by imitation, forming an association between the sight of the object and the act towards it through an idea gained from watching you. You may have caused his act simply by attracting his attention to the object. Perhaps if you had pointed at it or held it passively in your hand, you would have brought to pass just the same action on his part. There are several cases among my records where an act which an animal failed totally to do of himself was done after I had so attracted his attention to the object concerned.

Throughout all the time that I had my monkeys under observation I never noticed in their general behavior any act which seemed due to genuine imitation of me or the other persons about. I also gave them special opportunities to show such by means of a number of experiments of the following type: where an animal failed by himself to get into some box or operate some mechanism, I would operate it in his presence a number of times and then give him a chance to profit by the tuition. His failure might be due to (1) the absence of instinctive impulses to make the movement in that situation, (2) to lack of precision in the movement, (3) to lack of force, or (4) to failure to notice and attack some special part of the mechanism. An instance of (1) was the failure to push away from them a bar which held a door; an instance of (2) was the failure to pull a wire loop off a nail; an instance of (2) or (3) was the failure to pull up a bolt; an instance of (4) was the failure to pull up an inside bar. Failures due to (3) occur rarely in the case of such mechanisms as were used in my investigations.

The general method of experiment was to make sure that the animal would not of itself perform a certain act in a certain situation, then to make sure that his failure could not be remedied by attracting his attention to the object, then to perform the act for him a number of times, letting him get each time the food which resulted, and finally to see whether, having failed before the tuition, he would succeed after it. This sounds very simple, but such experiments are hard to carry out satisfactorily. If you try the animal enough times by himself to make quite sure that he will not of himself hit upon the act, you are likely to form in him the habit of meeting the particular situation in question with total disregard. His efforts having failed so often may be so inhibited that you could hardly expect any tuition to give them new life. The matter is worse if you add further enough trials to assure you that your attracting his attention to it has been unavailing. On the other hand, if you take failure in five or ten minutes to mean inability, and from subsequent success after imitation argue that imitation was efficient, you have to face the numerous cases where animals which have failed in ten minutes have succeeded in later unaided trials. With dogs and cats this does not much matter, because they are steady performers, and their conduct in one short trial tells you what to expect with some probability. But the monkeys are much more variable and are so frequently distracted that one feels much less confidence in his predictions. Moreover, you cannot be at all sure of having attracted a monkey's attention to an object unless he *does* touch it. Suppose, for example, a monkey has failed to even touch a bar though you have put a bit of food on it repeatedly. It is quite possible that he may look at and take the food and not notice the bar, and the fact that after such tuition he still fails to push or pull the bar may mean simply that it has not caught his notice. I have, therefore, preferred in most cases to give the animals only a brief period of trial to test their ability by their own unaided efforts and to omit the attempts to test the efficacy of attracting their attention to the vital point in the mechanism.

This makes the results appear less elegant and definitive but really increases their value for purposes of interpretation.

The thoughtful reader will not expect from my experiments any perfectly rigorous demonstration of either the presence or the absence of imitation of human acts as a means of learning. The general trend of the evidence, it seems to me, is decidedly towards justifying the hypothesis that the monkeys did not learn acts from seeing me do them.

I will first describe a sample experiment and then present a summary of all those made.

On January 12th I put box Epsilon (push down) in No. 3's cage, the door of the box being open. I put a bit of food in the box. No. 3 reached in and took it. This was repeated three times. I then put in a bit of food and closed the door. No. 3 pulled and bit the box, turned it over, fingered and bit at the hole where the lever was, but did not succeed in getting the door open. After ten minutes I took the box out. Later I took No. 3 out and let him sit on my knees (I sitting on the floor with the box in front of us). I would then put my hand out toward the box and when he was looking at it would insert my finger and depress the lever with as evident a movement as I could. The door, of course, opened, and No. 3 put his arm in and took the bit of food. I then put in another, closed the door and depressed the lever as before. No. 3 watched my hand pretty constantly, as all his experiences with me had made such watching profitable. After ten such trials he was put back in the cage and the box put in with a large piece of food in it and its door closed. No. 3 failed in five minutes and the box was taken out. He was shown fifteen times more and then left to try himself. I tried him for a couple of minutes under just the same circumstances as existed during the tuition, *i.e.* he on the floor by me, the box in front.   In this trial and in a five-minute trial inside his cage he failed to open the door or to differ in any essential respect from his behavior before tuition.

No. 1 saw me do 9 different acts and No. 3, 7, which they had failed of themselves to do.[1]   After from 1 to 40 chances to imitate me they still failed to operate at all 11 of these mechanisms.   In the case of 3 out of 5 that were worked the act was not the same as that taught.   No. 1, who saw me pull a nail out by taking the end of it and pulling the nail away from the box, himself put his hand round the nail and wriggled it out by pulling his hand back and forth.   No. 3, who saw me pull a bolt up with my fingers, succeeded by jerking and yanking the door until he shook the bolt up. He saw me pull a hook out of an eye, but he succeeded by pulling at a bar to which it was attached.   In the case of one of the two remaining acts (No. 3 with *nail chute*) the act was done once and never again, though ample opportunity was given and tuition continued.   It could, therefore, hardly have been due to an idea instilled by the tuition. The remaining case, No. 1, with loop, must, I think, be attributed to accident, especially since No. 3 failed to profit

[1] The acts and the number of chances to see me do each and the results were as follows; details can be found on the table on page 226.   F = failed after tuition.

No. 1. — MM	21 F	No. 3. — Theta	25 did in 3.00.
Theta	5 F	QQ	40 F
QQ	10 F	Gamma 30 F	
RR	4 F		
W	9 did in .22	Epsilon	25 F
Delta	15 F	QQ (ff)	5 F
Epsilon	40 F	QQ (c)	20 F, did in 1.30, F, 5 F, 5 F
QQ (f)	15 F	QQ e	5 F, did in 2.00
QQ (c)	1 did in 2.20		

by precisely the same sort of tuition with precisely the same act.

Nor is there any evidence to show that although tuition failed to cause successes where unaided effort failed, it yet caused attempts which would not otherwise have occurred. Out of fifteen cases where such might have appeared, there were only three where it is possible to claim that they did. No one of these three is a sure case. With RR (wood plug) No. 1 did seem to pull the plug more definitely after seeing me than before. With QQ (c) (nail chute) and MM (bolt at top) he may possibly have done so.

In 5 cases I tried the influence of seeing me make the movement on animals who had done the act of themselves, the aim being to see whether there would be a marked shortening of the time, a change in their way of operating the mechanism or an attempt at such change. I will give the essential facts from the general table on pages 226–229.

(*a*) No. 1 had succeeded in pulling in the box by the upper string in OOO (upper string box) in 2.20 and then failed in 3.00. I showed him 4 times. He failed in 10. I showed him 4 more times. He failed in 10. I showed him 4 more times. He succeeded in .20. No change in manner of act or objects attacked, though my manner was different from his.

(*b*) No. 1 had succeeded in QQ (a) (chute bar) in 8.00. I showed him 20 times. He failed in 10. I showed him 10 more times. He succeeded in 2.00. I showed him 10 more times. He succeeded in 50 seconds. No change in his manner of performance or in the object attacked, though my manner was different from his.

(*c*) No. 1 had succeeded in 3.00, .25, .07, .25, .20, .06 and .09 with QQ (b) (chute bar double) and then failed in 5.00. I showed him 10 times. He then failed in 5 twice, succeeded in 3.00, and failed in 5 again. No change in manner of performance or in the object attacked, though my manner was different from his.

(*d*) No. 3 had the following record in box **Delta**: —

> 2.00 (pushed with head)
> 3.20 (pushed with head)
> 30 F
> 10 F
> 10 F
> 2.10 (pulled wire and door).

I showed him 20 times by pushing the bar to the right with my finger. He succeeded in 8.00 and 8.00 by pulling the wire and the door. No change in object attacked.

(*e*) No. 2 had failed twice in 5 with chute QQ (ff) (chute string wire) and succeeded once in 2.00 by a strong pull on the wire itself, not the loop. I showed him 5 times, pulling the loop off the nail. He then failed in 5. There was no change in the objects attacked.

These records show no signs of any influence of the tuition that are not more probably signs of something else. We cannot attribute the rapid decrease in time taken in (*b*) to the tuition until we know the time-curve for the same process without tuition.

The systematic experiments designed to detect the presence of ability to learn from human beings are thus practically unanimous against it. So, too, was the general behavior of the monkeys, though I do not consider the failure of the animals to imitate common human acts as of much importance save as a rebuke to the story-tellers and casual observers. The following facts are samples: The door of No. 1's cage was closed by an iron hoop with a slit in it through which a staple passed, the door being held by a stick of wood thrust through the staple. No. 1 saw me open the door of his and other cages by taking out sticks hundreds of times, but though he escaped from his cage a dozen times in other ways, he never took the stick out and to my knowledge never tried to. I myself and visitors smoked a good deal in the monkeys' presence, but a cigar or cigarette given to them was always treated like anything else.

IMITATION OF OTHER MONKEYS

It would theoretically seem far more likely that the monkeys should learn from watching each other than from watching human beings, and experimental determinations of such ability are more important than those described in the last section as contributions both to genetic psychology and to natural history. I regret that the work I have been able to do in the study of this phase of the mental life of the monkeys has been very limited and in many ways unsatisfactory.

We should expect to find the tendency to imitation more obvious in the case of young and parents than elsewhere. I have had no chance to observe such cases. We should expect closely associated animals, such as members of a common troop or animals on friendly terms, to manifest it more than others. Unfortunately, two of my monkeys, by the time I was ready to make definite experiments, were on terms of war. The other had then become so shy that I could not confidently infer inability to do a thing from actual failure to do it. He showed no evidence of learning from his mates. I have, therefore, little evidence of a quantitative objective nature to present and shall have in the end to ask the reader to take some opinions without verifiable proofs.

My reliable experiments, five in number, were of the following nature. A monkey who had failed of himself (and often also after a chance to learn from me or from being put

through the act) would be put where he could see another
do the act and get a reward (food) for it. He would then be
given a chance to do it himself, and note would be taken of
his success or failure, and of whether his act was the same
as that of his model in case he succeeded, and of whether he
tried that act more than before the tuition in case he tried
it and failed. The results are given in Table 11.

In the fourth experiment No. 1 showed further that the
tuition did not cause his successes in that after some successes further tuition did not improve him.

There is clearly no evidence here of any imitation of No. 1
by No. 3. There was also apparently nothing like purposive
watching on the part of No. 3. He seemed often to see No.
1 open the box or work the chute mechanism, but without
special interest.

This lack of any special curiosity about the doings of their
own species characterized the general behavior of all three of
my monkeys and in itself lessens the probability that they
learn much from one another. Nor did there appear, in the
course of the three months and more the animals were together, any signs of imitation. There were indeed certain
notable instances of the lack of it in circumstances which
one would suppose would be favorable cases for it.

For instance: No. 2 was very timid. No. 1 was perfectly
tame from the first day No. 2 was with me, and No. 3 became tame shortly after. No. 2 saw Nos. 1 and 3 come to me,
be played with, fed and put through experiments, yet he
never did the same nor did he abate a jot or tittle from his
timidity save in so far as I sedulously rewarded any chance
advances of his. Conversely No. 1 and No. 3 seemed uninfluenced by the fear and shyness of No. 2. No. 2's cage
was between No. 1's and No. 3's, and they were for three
weeks incessantly making hostile demonstrations toward

TABLE 11

SUBJECT, DATE, ACT	TIME TRIED ALONE, WITH RESULT	No. OF TIMES IMITATEE DID	RESULT AFTER CHANCE FOR IMITATION	SIMILARITY OR DISSIMILARITY OF ACT	SIMILAR ACT ATTEMPTED, T OUGH UNSUCCESSFULLY IN CASES WHERE IT HAD NOT BEEN BEFORE TRAINING	GENERAL JUDGMENT AS TO INFLUENCE OF TRAINING
No. 3. Dec. 17, 1900. VV (wire loop)	50 F	43	55 F		No.	None.
No. 3. Jan. 15, 1901. QQ (c) (nail chute)	91 F 1.30	75	35 F		No.	None.
No. 3. Jan. 21, 1901. Gamma (wind)	63 F	43	5 F 9.00 6.00	Dissimilar.	No.	None.
No. 3. Jan. 21, 1901. QQ (ff) (string chute with wire)	20 F 2.00	30	1.30 .40 .35 5 F	Dissimilar.	No.	None.
No. 3. Jan. 23, 1901. QQ (chute).	1.15 F.	40	10 F		No.	None.

each other, jumping, chattering, scowling, etc. No. 2 never did anything of the sort. Again, seeing No. 3 eat meat did not lead No. 1 to take it; nor did seeing No. 1 retreat in fright from a bit of absorbent cotton lead No. 3 to avoid it.

Nothing in my experience with these animals, then, favors the hypothesis that they have any general ability to learn to do things from seeing others do them. The question is still an open one, however, and a much more extensive study of it should be made, especially of the possible influence of imitation in the case of acts already familiar either as wholes or in their elements.

LEARNING APART FROM MOTOR IMPULSES

The reader of my monograph, 'Animal Intelligence,' will recall that the experiments there reported seemed to show that the chicks, cats and dogs had only slight and sporadic, if any, ability to form associations except such as contained some actual motor impulse. They failed to form such associations between the sense-impressions and ideas of movements as would lead them to make the movements without having themselves previously in those situations given the motor impulses to the movements. They could not, for instance, learn to do a thing from having been put through it by me.

The monkeys Nos. 1 and 3 were tested in a similar way with a number of different acts. The general conclusion from the experiments, the details of which will be given presently, is that the monkeys are not proved to have the power of forming associations of ideas to any greater extent than the other mammals, that they do not demonstrably learn to do things from seeing or feeling themselves make the movement. An adult human being whose hand was taken and made to push in a bar or pull back a bolt would thereby learn to do it for himself. Cats and dogs would not, and the monkeys are not proved to do so. On the other hand, it is impossible for me to say, as of the dogs and cats, that the monkeys are proved not to do so. In a few cases the animals did perform acts after having been put through them which they had failed to perform when left to their own trial and success method. In the majority of cases they did not. And in some of these latter cases failure seemed so improbable in case the animal really had the power of getting an idea of the act and proceeding from idea to execution, that one is inevitably led to some explanation for the few successes other than the presence of 'ideas.'

The general manner of making these experiments was like that in the case of the cats and dogs, save that the monkey's paw was used to open the box from the outside instead of from the inside, and that the monkeys were also put through the acts necessary to operate some of the chute mechanisms. Tests parallel to that of comparing the behavior of kittens who had themselves gone into boxes with those who were dropped in by me were made in the following manner. I would carry a monkey from his cage and put him in some conspicuous place (*e.g.* on the top of a chair) and then give him a bit of food. This I would repeat a number of times. Then I would turn him loose in the room to see whether he had acquired an idea of being on the chair which would lead him to himself go to the chair. I would, in order to tell whether his act, in case he did so, was the result of random activities or was really due to his tuition, leave him alone for 5 or 10 minutes before the tuition. If he got on the chair afterwards when he had not before, or got on it much sooner, it would tend to show that the idea of getting food on that chair was present and effective. We may call these last the 'on chair' type of experiments.

A sample experiment with a box is the following:—

On January 4, 1901, box Delta (push back) was put in No. 1's cage. He failed in 5, though he was active in trying to get in for about 4 minutes of the time and pulled and pushed the bar a great deal, though up and down and out instead of back. In his aimless pushings and pullings he nearly succeeded. He failed in 5 in a second trial also. I then opened the door of the cage, sat down beside it, held out my hand, and when he came to me took his right paw and with it (he being held in front of the box) pushed the bar back (and pulled the door open in those cases when it did not fall open of itself). He reached in and took the food and went back to the top of his cage and ate it. (No. 1 generally did this, while No. 3 generally stayed by me.) I then tried him alone; result 10 F; no activity at all. On January 5th I put the box in; result 10 F. He was fairly active. He pulled at the bar but mostly from a position on the top of the box and with his left hand; no attempts like the one I had tried to teach him. Being left alone he failed in 5. Being tried again with the door of the cage open and me sitting as I had done while putting him through the act, he succeeded in 7.00 by pushing the bar with his head in the course of efforts to poke his head in at the door. I then put him through the act 10 times and left him to himself. He failed in 5.00; no activity. I then sat down by the cage as when teaching him. He failed in 5; little activity. Later in the day I put him through the act 10 times and then left him to himself. He failed in 5; little activity. I sat down as before. He failed in five; little activity. On January 6th I put him through the act 10 times and then left him. He failed in 10. This was repeated later in the day with the same result.

Record: — By himself, 10 F.   Put through 80 times.   F 65 (a) [the (a) refers to a note of his unrepeated chance success with his head].   No similar act unsuccessfully attempted. Influence of tuition, none.

With the chute mechanisms the record would be of the same nature.   With them I put the animal through generally by taking his paw, held out through the wire netting of the cage, and making the movement with it.   In one experiment (No. 3 with QQ chute) the first 58 trials were made by taking the monkey outside the cage and holding him instead of having him put his paw through the netting for me to take.

Many of the experiments were with mechanisms which had previously been used in experiments concerning the ability to learn from seeing me operate them.   And the following Table (12) includes the results of experiments of both sorts.   The results of experiments of the 'on chair' type are in Table 13.   In cases where the same apparatus was used for both purposes, the sort of training which was given first is that where an A is placed.

In the first four experiments with No. 1 there was some struggling and agitation on his part while being held and put through the act.   After that there was none in his case except occasional playfulness, and there was never any with No. 3 after the first third of the first experiment.   The monkeys soon formed the habit of keeping still, because it was only when still that I put them through the act and that food resulted.   After you once get them so that they can be held and their arms taken without their clinging to you, they quickly learn to adapt themselves to the experiments.

With No. 1, out of 8 cases where he had of himself failed (in five of the cases he had also failed after being shown by me), he succeeded after being put through (13, 21, 51, 10, 7,

TABLE 12

Subject. Date. Act	Times Tried Alone, With Result	Number of Times Attention Attracted	Result	Number of Times Shown by Me	Result in Trials After Being Shown by Me	Number of Times Put Through the Act	Result in Trials After Being Put Through the Act	Comparison of Act Used with Act Taught	Similar Act Attempted Though Unsuccessfully	Act Done Once or More, but Not Repeated in Spite of Repeated Tuition
No. 1, Jan. 7, 1900, PP (string across)	10 F 10 F			21A	150 F 10 F 10 F	13	10 F		No.	
No. 1, Jan. 17, 1900, MM (bolt at top)	15 F	2				21	10 F		(?)	
No. 1, Feb. 24, 1900, OOO (upper string)	2.20 3 F		5 F	4 4 } 12 4 4	.20			Partly similar.	No.	
No. 1, Mar. 24, 1900, QQ (chute)	120 F 10 F			10A	.22 60 F	10	30.00	Dissimilar.	No.	
No. 1, Apr. 5, 1900, RR (wood plug)	10 F			1A 1 1 1 4	2 F 2 F 2 F 5 F .22	7 2	2.20 2.00	Similar.	Yes(?)	
No. 1, Oct. 20, 1900, VV (loop)	10 F 10 F 10 F 10 F							Similar.		
No. 1, Nov. 19, 1900, Theta (new bolt)	10 F			5	10 F	51A	132 F		No.	
No. 1, Jan. 4, 1901, Delta (push back)	10 F			15	10 F	80A	65 F[1]		No.	

[1] He did push it once with his nose.

TABLE 12 — *Continued*

No. 1, Jan. 6, 1901, QQ (a) (single wind chute)	8.00			40	10 F 2.00 .50			Dissimilar.		Yes.
No. 1, Jan. 7, 1901, Zeta (side plug new)	5 F 1.10					20	im. im.	?		
No. 1, Jan. 9, 1901, QQ (b) (2½ wind chute)	3.00 to .06 5 F			10	5 F 5 F 3.00 5 F					
No. 1, Jan. 11, 1901, QQ (c) (nail chute)	5 F 5 F	5	5 F	1 [1]	2.20			Dissimilar.	No.	Yes.
No. 1, Jan. 12, 1901, Epsilon (push down)	5 F 10 F			25A 15	10 F 10 F 10 F	10 10	5 F 10 F	Dissimilar.	No.	Yes. [2]
No. 1, Jan. 16, 1901, QQ (d) (pull chute)	5 F 5 F	5	3.30 .10	15						
No. 1, Jan. 17, 1901, QQ (f) (string chute)	5 F 5 F	5	5 F	15A	5 F 5 F	10	5 F			
No. 1, Jan. 18, 1901, QQ (e) (hook chute)	5 F	3	im.							

[1] I inadvertently pulled the nail out in one of five cases when I was fingering it to see if attracting his attention to it would lead to the act.
[2] Not significant. Was temporary. Due to inattention.

TABLE 12 — *Continued*

SUBJECT. DATE. ACT	TIMES TRIED ALONE, WITH RESULT	NUMBER OF TIMES ATTENTION AT-TRACTED	RESULT	NUMBER OF TIMES SHOWN BY ME	RESULT IN TRIALS AFTER BEING SHOWN BY ME	NUMBER OF TIMES PUT THROUGH THE ACT	RESULT IN TRIALS AFTER BEING PUT THROUGH THE ACT	COMPARISON OF ACT USED WITH ACT TAUGHT	SIMILAR ACT AT-TEMPTED THOUGH UNSUCCESSFULLY	ACT DONE ONCE OR MORE, BUT NOT REPEATED IN SPITE OF RE-PEATED TUITION
No. 3, Dec. 17, 1900, QQ (chute)	60 F	3	60 F	10A, 30	5 F, 30 F	113	90 F		(?)	
No. 3, Dec. 17, 1900, VV (loop)	10 F, 20 F			30	30 F	23	20 F		No.	
No. 3, Jan. 4, 1901, Delta (push back)	10 F, 2.10 (by pulling string)			20	8.00[1], 8.00[1]	5A, 5, 15, 5	2.00[2], 3.20, 30 F, 10 F	Dissimilar.	No.	
No. 3, Jan. 4, 1901, Gamma (wind)	10 F			30	10 F, 10 F	20 A	5 F, 8 F		No.	
No. 3, Jan. 8, 1901, Theta (bolt at top)	10 F[3]			25	6 F			Dissimilar.		
No. 3, Jan. 9, 1901, QQ (a) (chute bar)	10 F				3.00[4]	10, 10, 10, 10	.40, 1.00, 1.00, 1.00	?	No complete circle.	
No. 3, Jan. 9, 1901, QQ (b) (2½ wind chute)	10 F			20	8 F, 8 F		5 F	Dissimilar.		Yes.

[1] Pulled wire and door.   [2] Pushed with head by chance.   [3] Reached in at 9:30 and took out the banana, which I replaced.
[4] Did by constant pulling at the door.

TABLE 12 — *Continued*

No. 3, Jan. 11, 1901, QQ (c) (nail chute)	5 F, 5 F	10	5 F, 12 F[1]	25 A	5 F, 5 F, 1.30, 5 F, 10 F	45	38 F, 10 F		No.	Yes.
No. 3, Jan. 15, 1901, Epsilon (push down)	10 F			25 A	5 F, 5 F	20	11.00, 30 F, 10 F	?	No.	Yes.
No. 3, Jan. 16, 1901, QQ (e) (hook chute)	5 F	5	5 F	5 A	2.00, 1.25, 1.20	10, 15	.10, .10	Dissimilar.	No.	
No. 3, Jan. 19, 1901, QQ (ff) (string chute with wire)	5 F, 5 F, 2.00[2]		5	5 A	5 F	7, 8, 12	5 F, 5 F, 3.00, 5 F, 5 F	Dissimilar.	No.	
No. 3, Jan. 22, 1901, WW (bar inside)	5 F, previously some, 40.00F					10	6.00[3], 7.00[3]	Dissimilar.	No.	

[1] Did touch nail four times.
[2] Did by pulling at the door till the bar was worked around.
[3] Did by pulling hard on wire (not loop); the loop got loose from nail.

80, and 10 times) in two cases (QQ (chute) and RR (wood plug). The act was unlike the one taught him in the former case.

In only one case (bolt at top) out of eight was there possibly any attempt at the act after he had been put through which had not been made before. The 'yes or ?' in the table with RR was a case occurring after the imitation of me but before the putting No. 1 through.

Out of 6 cases where he had himself failed, No. 3 succeeded (after being put through 113, 23, 20, 10, 10, 20 and 10 times) in 3 cases (chute bar, push down and bar inside). The act was dissimilar in all three cases, bearing absolutely no resemblance in one case. There was no unsuccessful attempt at the act taught him in any of the cases. With the chute he did finger the bar after tuition where he had not done so before, but it was probably an accidental result of his holding his hand out toward it for me to take as he had formed the habit of doing. In the case of box Epsilon (push down), with which he succeeded by pushing his hand in above the lever (an act which though unlike that taught him might be by some considered to be due to an idea gained from the tuition), he failed entirely after further tuition (15 times).

Like the dogs and cats, then, the monkeys seemed unable to learn to do things from being put through them. We may now examine those which they did do of themselves before tuition and ask whether they learned the more rapidly thereby or modified their behavior in ways which might be due to the tuition. There are too few cases and no chance for comparison on the first point; on the second the records are unanimous in showing no change in the method of operating the mechanisms due to the tuition.

As in Table 9, figures followed by F mean that in that

length of time the animal failed.   Figures without an F denote the time taken by the animal to operate the mechanism.

As a supplement to Table 12 I have made a summary of the cases where the animals did succeed after tuition, that shows the nature of the act shown them as compared with the act they made use of.

SUPPLEMENT TO TABLE 12

APPARATUS	MODEL GIVEN OR ACT PUT THROUGH	ACT OF NO. 1	ACT OF NO. 3
OOO	To pull upper string.	Pulled both strings alternately, but upper enough more to succeed.	
QQ	To push bar in.	Inserted fingers between bar and its slot and pulled and pushed vaguely.	
RR	To pull plug out with right hand.	Pulled and bit.	
VV	To pull loop off nail with right hand.	*Similar*.	
QQ (a)	To pull bar around toward him.	Pulled back and forth indiscriminately.	Pulled back and forth indiscriminately.
QQ (b)	To pull bar around toward him in $2\frac{1}{2}$ continuous revolutions.	Pulled back and forth indiscriminately.	
QQ (c)	To take nail and pull directly outward.	Pulled back and forth.	*Similar* or nearly so.
Delta	To push bar to right with right hand.		Did before tuition by pulling wire; after tuition by chance movement of head.
Theta	To pull bolt up with right hand.		Pulled door and worked bolt loose.

APPARATUS	MODEL GIVEN OR ACT PUT THROUGH	ACT OF NO. 1	ACT OF NO. 3
Epsilon	To stand in front, insert fingers of right hand and press lever down.		Inserted arm in general activity while on top of the box.
QQ (e)	To pull hook down.		Pulled at the lever and hook in a general attack on the apparatus.
QQ (ff)	To pull wire loop off nail with right hand.		Pulled outward on the lever which pushed the banana down the chute so hard as to pull it off its pivot.
WW	To stand on top of box, reach right hand down and pull bar up.		Pulled at door until bar worked out of its catch.

I have kept the results of the tests of the 'on chair' type separate from the others because they may be tests of a different thing and surely are subject to different conditions.

They were tests of the animals' ability to form the habit of going to a certain place by reason of having been *carried* there and securing food thereby. I would leave the animal loose in the room, and if he failed in 5 or 10 minutes to go to the place of his own accord, would put him back in his cage; if he did go of his own accord, I would note the time. Then I would take him, carry him to the place, and feed him. After doing this 10 times I would turn him loose again and see whether the idea of being fed in such and such a place was present and active in making him go to the place. In such tests we are absolutely sure that the animal can without any difficulty perform the necessary movements and would in case the proper stimulus to set them off appeared, if, for instance, a bit of food on one of the places to which he was to go caught his eye. In so far forth the tests were favorable cases for learning. On the other hand, the situation associated with getting food may have been in these cases not the mere 'being on box' but the whole previous experience 'being carried while clinging and being put or let jump on a box.' In this respect the tests may have been less favorable than the acts where getting food was always the direct sequent of the act of going into the box.

The experiments were : —

A. Carrying the animal and putting him on a chair.

B. Carrying the animal and putting him on a pile of boxes.

C. Carrying the animal and putting him on the top of a sewing machine.

D. Carrying the animal and putting him on the middle of a board 6 feet long, stretched horizontally across the room, 3 feet from the floor.

E. Carrying the animal and putting him on the side of the cage, head down.

The results are given in Table 13.

The size of the room in which I worked and other practical difficulties prevented me from extending these experiments. As they stand, no stable judgments can be inferred from them. It should be noted that in the successful cases there were no other signs of the presence of the idea 'food when there' than the mere going to a certain place. The animal did not wait at the place more than a second or two, did not look at me or show any signs of expecting anything.

Although, as I noted in the early part of this monograph, there were occasionally phenomena in the general behavior of the monkeys which of themselves impressed one as being suggestive of an ideational life, the general run of their

TABLE 13

EXPERIMENT AND DATE	ANIMAL	RESULTS BEFORE TRAINING	NUMBER OF TIMES PUT THROUGH	RESULTS AFTER TRAINING
A. Jan. 22, 1901	No. 1.	5 F	10	1.00
				3.00
Jan. 22, 1901	No. 1.	5 F	10	im.
				3.30
Jan. 23, 1901	No. 3.	5 F	10	3.30
		5 F		
B. Jan. 26, 1901	No. 1.	10 F	10 and 5	10 F 5 F
	No. 3.	5 F	10	5 F
			10	5 F
C. Jan. 27, 1901	No. 1.	5 F	10	3.00
D. Jan. 27, 1901	No. 1.	·3.20	10	5 F
E. Jan. 26, 1901	No. 3.	5 F	5	5 F

learning apart from the specific experiments described was certainly confined to the association of impulses of their own with certain situations. The following examples will suffice : —

In getting them so that they would let themselves be handled it was of almost no service to *take* them and feed them while holding them or otherwise make that state pleasant for them. By far the best way is to wait patiently till they do come near, then feed them ; wait patiently till they do take hold of your arm, then feed them. If you do take them and hold them partly by force, you must feed them only when they are comparatively still. In short, in taming them one comes unconsciously to adopt the method of rewarding certain of their impulses rather than certain *conditions* which might be associated in their minds with ideas, had they such.

After No. 1 and No. 3 had both reached a point where both could hardly be gotten to leave me and go back into their cages or down to the floor of the room, where they evidently enjoyed being held by me, they still did not climb upon me. The idea of clinging to me was either absent or impotent to cause them to act. What they did do was, in the case of No. 1, to jump about, pawing around in the air, until I caught an arm or leg, to which stimulus he had by dint of the typical sort of animal association learned to react by jumping to my arm and clinging there; in the case of No. 3, to stand still until I held my arm right in front of him (if he were in his cage) or to come and stand on his hind legs in front of me (if he were out on the floor). In both cases No. 3's act was one which had been learned by my rewarding his impulses. I often tried, at this period of their intimacy with me, this instructive experiment. The monkey would be clinging to me so that I could hardly tear him away. I would do so, and he would, if dropped loose from me, make no efforts to get back.

I have already mentioned my failure to get the animals to put out their right hands through the netting after they had long done so with their left hands. With No. 3 I tried putting my fingers through and poking the arm out and then making the movement with it. He profited little if any by this tuition. Had I somehow induced him to do it himself, a few trials would have been sufficient to get the habit well under way.

Monkey No. 1 apparently enjoyed scratching himself. Among the stimuli which served to set off this act of scratching was the irritation from tobacco smoke. If any one would blow smoke in No. 1's face, he would blink his eyes and scratch himself, principally in the back. After a time he got in the habit of coming to the front of his cage when any one was smoking and making such movements and sounds as in his experience had attracted attention and

caused the smoker to blow in his face. He was often given a lighted cigar or cigarette to test him for imitation. He formed the habit of rubbing it on his back. After doing so he would scratch himself with great vigor and zest. He came to do this always when the proper object was given him. I have recounted all this to show that the monkey enjoyed scratching himself. *Yet he apparently never scratched himself except in response to some sensory stimulus.* He was apparently incapable of thinking 'scratch' and so doing. Yet the act was quite capable of association with circumstances with which as a matter of hereditary organization it had no connection. For by taking a certain well-defined position in front of his cage and feeding him whenever he did scratch himself I got him to always scratch within a few seconds after I took that position.

GENERAL MENTAL DEVELOPMENT OF THE MONKEYS

It is to be hoped that the growing recognition of the worth of comparative and genetic studies will lead to investigations of the mental make-up of other species of monkeys, and to the careful overhauling of the work done so far, including these rather fragmentary studies of mine. Work with three monkeys of one species, especially when no general body of phenomena, such as one has at hand in the case of domestic animals, can be used as a means of comparison, must necessarily be of limited application in all its details and of insecure application even in its general features. What I shall say concerning the advance in the mental development of the monkeys over that of other mammals may then be in strictness true of only my three subjects, and it may be left to the judgment of individuals to extend my conclusions as far as seems to them likely. To me it seems fairly likely that the very general mental traits which the research has demonstrated hold true with little variation in the monkeys in general.

The monkeys represent progress in mental development from the generalized mammalian type toward man : —

1. In their sensory equipment, in the presence of focalized vision.

2. In their motor equipment, in the coördinated move-ments of the hand and the eye.

3. In their instincts or inherited nervous connections, in their general physical and mental activity.

4. In their method of learning or associative processes; in —

    a. Quicker formation of associations,

    b. Greater number of associations,

    c. Greater delicacy of associations,

    d. Greater complexity of associations,

    e. Greater permanence of associations.

The fact of (1) is well known to comparative anatomists. Its importance in mental development is perhaps not real-ized, but appears constantly to a systematic student.

(2) is what accounts for much of the specious appearance of human ways of thinking in the monkeys and becomes in its human extension the handy tool for much of our intel-lectual life. It is in great measure the prerequisite of 4 *c*.

(3) accounts for the rest of such specious appearances, is at the basis of much of 4 *b*, presages the similar though extended instincts of the human being, which I believe are the leading efficient causes of human mental capacity, and is thus the great mental bond which would justify the in-clusion of monkeys and man in a common group if we were to classify animals on the basis of mental characteristics.

Even the casual observer, if he has any psychological insight, will be struck by the general, aimless, intrinsically valuable (to the animal's feelings) physical activities of a monkey compared with the specialized, definitely aroused, utilitarian activities of a dog or cat. Watch the latter and he does but few things, does them in response to obvious sense presentations, does them with practical consequences of food, sex-indulgence, preparation for adult battles, etc. If nothing that appeals to his special organization comes up, he does nothing. Watch a monkey and you cannot enumerate the things he does, cannot discover the stimuli to which he reacts, cannot conceive the *raison d'être* of his pursuits. Everything appeals to him. He likes to be active for the sake of activity.

The observer who has proper opportunities and takes proper pains will find this intrinsic interest to hold of mental activity as well. No. 1 happened to hit a projecting wire so as to make it vibrate. He repeated this act hundreds of times in the few days following. He did not, could not, eat, make love to, or get preliminary practice for the serious battles of life out of, that sound. But it did give him mental food, mental exercise. Monkeys seem to enjoy strange places; they revel, if I may be permitted an anthropomorphism, in novel objects. They like to have feelings as they do to make movements. The fact of mental life is to them its own reward.

It is beyond question rash for any one to venture hypotheses concerning the brain parallel of mental conditions, most of all for the ignoramus in the comparative histology of the nervous system, but one cannot help thinking that the behavior of the monkeys points to a cerebrum that is no longer a conservative machine for making a few well-defined sorts of connections between sense-impressions and acts, that is not only fitted to do more delicate work in parts, but is also alive, tender all over, functioning throughout, set off in action by anything and everything. And if one adds coördinations allowing a freedom and a differentiation of action of the muscles used in speech comparable to that already present in connection with the monkey's hand, he may well ask, "What more of a nervous mechanism do you need to parallel the behavior of the year-old child?" However, this is not the place to speculate upon the importance to human development of our instinctive aimless activity, physical and mental, or to describe further its similarity and evident phylogenetic relationship to the instinctive behavior of the monkeys. Elsewhere I shall undertake that task.

4. In their method of learning, the monkeys do not advance far beyond the generalized mammalian type, but in their proficiency in that method they do. They seem at least to form associations very much faster, and they form very many more. They also seem superior in the delicacy and in the complexity of the associations formed and the connections seem to be more permanent.

This progress may seem, and doubtless will to the thinker who looks upon the human intellect as a collection of functions of which ideation, judgment and reasoning are chief, to be slight. To my mind it is not so in reality. For it seems to me highly probable that the so-called ' higher ' intellectual processes of human beings are but secondary results of the general function of having free ideas and that this general function is the result of the formation after the fashion of the animals of a very great number of associations. I should therefore say, "Let us not wonder at the comparative absence of free ideas in the monkeys, much less at the absence of inferences or concepts. Let us not wonder that the only demonstrable intellectual advance of the monkeys over the mammals in general is the change from a few, narrowly confined, practical associations to a multitude of all sorts, for that may turn out to be at the bottom the only *demonstrable advance of man*, an advance which in connection with a brain acting with increased delicacy and irritability, brings in its train the functions which mark off human mental faculty from that of all other animals.

The typical process of association described in Chapter II has since been found to exist among reptiles (by Mr. R. M. Yerkes) and among fishes (by myself). It seems fairly likely that not much more characterizes the primates. If such work as that of Lubbock and the Peckhams holds its own against the critical studies of Bethe, this same process exists in the insects. Yerkes and Bosworth think they have demonstrated its presence in the crayfish. Even if we regard the learning of the invertebrates as problematic, still this process is the most comprehensive and important thing in mental life. I have already hinted that we ought to turn our views of human psychology upside down and study what is now casually referred to in a chapter on habit or on the development of the will, as the general psychological law, of which the commonly named processes are derivatives. When this is done, we shall not only relieve human mentality from its isolation and see its real relationships with other forms ; we may also come to know more about it, may even elevate our psychologies to the explanatory level and connect mental processes with nervous activities without arousing a sneer from the logician or a grin from the neurologist.

CHAPTER VI

Laws and Hypotheses for Behavior

Laws of Behavior in General

Behavior is predictable. The first law of behavior, one fraction of the general law of the uniformity of nature, is that with life and mind, as with mass and motion, the same cause will produce the same effect, — that *the same situation will, in the same animal, produce the same response,* — and that *if the same situation produces on two occasions two different responses, the animal must have changed.*

Scientific students of behavior will, with few exceptions, accept this law in theory, but in practice we have not fully used it. We have too often been content to say that a man may respond in any one of several ways to the same situation, or may attend to one rather than another feature of the same object, without insisting that the man must in each case be different, and without searching for the differences in him which cause the different reactions.

The changes in an organism which make it respond differently on different occasions to the same situation range from temporary to permanent changes. Hunger, fatigue, sleep, and certain diseases on the one hand, and learning, immunity, growth and senility on the other, illustrate this range.

Behavior is predictable *without recourse to magical agencies*. It is, of course, the case that any given difference between the responses of an animal to the same situation depends upon some *particular* difference in the animal. Each immunity, for example, has its detailed representation in an altered condition of the blood or other bodily tissue. In general the changes in an animal which cause changes in its behavior to the same situation are fully enumerated in a list of the bodily changes concerned. That is, whatever changes may be supposed to have taken place in the animal's vital force, spiritual essence, or other magical bases for life and thought, are useless for scientific explanation and control of behavior.

No competent thinker probably doubts this in the case of such changes as are referred to by hunger, sleep, fatigue, so-called 'functional' diseases and immunity, and those who do doubt it in the case of mental growth and learning seem to represent an incomplete evolution from supernatural, or rather infrascientific, thinking. There may be in behavior a surplus beyond what would be predictable if the entire history of every atom in the body was known — a surplus necessarily attributable to changes in the animal's incorporeal structure. But scientific thinkers properly refuse to deliberately count upon such a surplus.

Every response or change in response of an animal is then the result of the interaction of its original knowable nature and the environment. This may seem too self-evident a corollary for mention. It should be so, but, unfortunately, it is not. Two popular psychological doctrines exist in defiance of it. One is the doctrine that the movements of early infancy are random, the original nature of the animal being entirely indifferent as to what movement shall be made upon a given stimulus. But no animal can have an original nature that does not absolutely prescribe just what the response shall be to every stimulus. If the movements are really random, they occur by virtue of some force that works at random.

If the movements are really the result of the action of the environment on the animal's nature, they are never random. A baby twiddles his thumbs or waves his legs for exactly the same sort of reason that a chick pecks at a worm or preens its wing.

The other doctrine which witnesses to neglect of the axiom that behavior is the creation of the environment, acting on the animal's nature, is the doctrine that the need for a certain behavior helps to create it, that being in a difficulty tends in and of itself to make an animal respond so as to end the difficulty.

The truth is that to a difficulty the animal responds by whatever its inherited and acquired nature has connected with the special form of difficulty and that in many animals the one response of those thus provided which relieves the difficulty is selected and connected more firmly with that difficulty's next appearance. The difficulty acts only as a stimulus to the animal's nature and its relief acts only as a premium to the connection whereby it was relieved. The law of original behavior, or the law of instinct, is then that *to any situation an animal will, apart from learning, respond by virtue of the inherited nature of its reception-, connection- and action-systems.*

The inquiry into the laws of learning to be made in this essay is limited to those aspects of behavior which the term has come historically to signify, that is, to intellect, skill, morals and the like.

For the purposes of this essay it is not necessary to decide just what features of an animal's behavior to include under intellect, skill, morals and the like. The statements to be made will fit any reasonable dividing line between behavior on the one side and mere circulation, digestion, excretion and the like on the other. There should in fact be no clear dividing line, since there is no clear gap between those activities which naturalists have come to call behavior and the others.

The discussion will include: First, a description of two laws of learning; second, an argument to prove that no additional forces are needed — that these two laws explain all learning; and third, an investigation of whether these two laws are reducible to more fundamental laws. I shall also note briefly the consequences of the acceptance of these laws in one sample case, that of the study of mental evolution.

PROVISIONAL LAWS OF ACQUIRED BEHAVIOR OR LEARNING

The Law of Effect is that: *Of several responses made to the same situation, those which are accompanied or closely followed by satisfaction to the animal will, other things being equal, be more firmly connected with the situation, so that, when it recurs, they will be more likely to recur; those which are accompanied or closely followed by discomfort to the animal will, other things being equal, have their connections with that situation weakened, so that, when it recurs, they will be less likely to occur. The greater the satisfaction or discomfort, the greater the strengthening or weakening of the bond.*

The Law of Exercise is that: *Any response to a situation will, other things being equal, be more strongly connected with the situation in proportion to the number of times it has been connected with that situation and to the average vigor and duration of the connections.*

These two laws stand out clearly in every series of experiments on animal learning and in the entire history of the management of human affairs. They give an account of learning that is satisfactory over a wide range of experience, so long as all that is demanded is a rough and general means of prophecy. We can, as a rule, get an animal to learn a given accomplishment by getting him to accomplish it, rewarding him when he does, and punishing him when he does not; or, if reward or punishment are kept indifferent, by getting him to accomplish it much oftener than he does any other response to the situation in question.

For more detailed and perfect prophecy, the phrases 'result in satisfaction' and 'result in discomfort' need further definition, and the other things that are to be equal need comment.

By a satisfying state of affairs is meant one which the animal does nothing to avoid, often doing such things as attain and preserve it. By a discomforting or annoying state of affairs is meant one which the animal commonly avoids and abandons.

The satisfiers for any animal in any given condition cannot be determined with precision and surety save by observation. Food when hungry, society when lonesome, sleep when fatigued, relief from pain, are samples of the common occurrence that what favors the life of the species satisfies its individual members. But this does not furnish a completely valid rule.

The satisfying and annoying are not synonymous with favorable and unfavorable to the life of either the individual or the species. Many animals are satisfied by deleterious conditions. Excitement, overeating, and alcoholic intoxication are, for instance, three very common and very potent satisfiers of man. Conditions useful to the life of the species in moderation are often satisfying far beyond their useful point: many conditions of great utility to the life of the species do not satisfy and may even annoy its members.

The annoyers for any animal follow the rough rule that

alterations of the animal's 'natural' or 'normal' structure —
as by cuts, bruises, blows, and the like, — and deprivations
of or interference with its 'natural' or 'normal' activities, —
as by capture, starvation, solitude, or indigestion, — are intolerable. But interference with the structure and functions by which the species is perpetuated is not a sufficient
criterion for discomfort. Nature's adaptations are too
crude.

Upon examination it appears that the pernicious states of
affairs which an animal welcomes are not pernicious *at the
time, to the neurones*. We learn many bad habits, such as
morphinism, because there is incomplete adaptation of all
the interests of the body-state to the temporary interest of
its ruling class, the neurones. So also the unsatisfying
goods are not goods to the neurones at the time. We neglect
many benefits because the neurones choose their immediate
advantage. The neurones must be tricked into permitting
the animal to take exercise when freezing or quinine when
in a fever, or to free the stomach from certain poisons.

Satisfaction and discomfort, welcoming and avoiding, thus
seem to be related to the maintenance and hindrance of the
life processes of the neurones rather than of the animal as a
whole, and to temporary rather than permanent maintenance and hindrance.

The chief life processes of a neurone concerned in learning
are absorption of food, excretion of waste, reception and
conduction of the nerve impulse, and modifiability or change
of connections. Of these only the latter demands comment.

The connections formed between situation and response
are represented by connections between neurones and neurones, whereby the disturbance or neural current arising in
the former is conducted to the latter across their synapses.
The strength or weakness of a connection means the greater

or less likelihood that the same current will be conducted from the former to the latter rather than to some other place. The strength or weakness of the connection is a condition of the synapse. What condition of the synapse it is remains a matter for hypothesis. Close connection might mean protoplasmic union, or proximity of the neurones in space, or a greater permeability of a membrane, or a lowered electrical resistance, or a favorable chemical condition of some other sort. Let us call this undefined condition which parallels the strength of a connection between situation and response the intimacy of the synapse. Then the modifiability or connection changing of a neurone equals its power to alter the intimacy of its synapses.

As a provisional hypothesis to account for what satisfies and what annoys an animal, I suggest the following: —

A neurone modifies the intimacy of its synapses so as to keep intimate those by whose intimacy its other life processes are favored and to weaken the intimacy of those whereby its other life processes are hindered. The animal's action-system as a whole consequently does nothing to avoid that response whereby the life processes of the neurones other than connection-changing are maintained, but does cease those responses whereby such life processes of the neurones are hindered.

This hypothesis has two important consequences. First: Learning by the law of effect is then more fully adaptive for the neurones in the changing intimacy of whose synapses learning consists, than for the animal as a whole. It is adaptive for the animal as a whole only in so far as his organization makes the neurones concerned in the learning welcome states of affairs that are favorable to his life and that of his species and reject those that are harmful.

Second: A mechanism in the neurones gives results in

the behavior of the animal as a whole that seem beyond mechanism. By their unmodifiable abandonment of certain specific conditions and retention of others, the animal as a whole can modify its behavior. Their one rule of conduct causes in him a countless complexity of habits. The learning of an animal is an instinct of its neurones.

I have limited the discussion to animals in whom the connection-system is a differentiated organ, the neurones. In so far as the law of effect operates in an animal whose connection-system is not anatomically distinguishable and is favored and hindered in its life by the same conditions that favor and hinder the life of the animal as a whole, the satisfying and annoying will be those states of affairs which the connection-system, whatever it be, maintains and abandons.

The other things that have to be equal in the case of the law of effect are: First, the frequency, energy and duration of the connection, — that is, the action of the law of exercise; second, the closeness with which the satisfaction is associated with the response; and, third, the readiness of the response to be connected with the situation.

The first of these accessory conditions requires no comment. A slightly satisfying or indifferent response made often may win a closer connection than a more satisfying response made only rarely.

The second is most clearly seen in the effect of increasing the interval between the response and the satisfaction or discomfort. Such an increase diminishes the rate of learning. If, for example, four boxes were arranged so that turning a button caused a door to open (and permit a cat to get freedom and food) in one, five, fifty and five hundred seconds, respectively, a cat would form the habit of prompt escape from the first box most rapidly and would almost certainly never form that habit in the case of the fourth.

The electric shock administered just as an animal starts on the wrong path or touches the wrong mechanism, is potent, but the same punishment administered ten or twenty seconds after an act will have little or no effect upon that act.

Close temporal sequence is not the only means of insuring the connection of the satisfaction with the response producing it. What is called attention to the response counts also. If a cat pushes a button around with its nose, while its main occupation, the act to which its general 'set' impels it, to which, we say, it is chiefly attentive, is that of clawing at an opening, it will be less aided in the formation of the habit than if it had been chiefly concerned in what its nose was doing. The successful response is as a rule only a part of all that the animal is doing at the time. In proportion as it is an eminent, emphatic part of it, learning is aided. Similarly discomfort eliminates most the eminent, emphatic features of the total response which it accompanies or shortly follows.

The third factor, the susceptibility of the response and situation to connection, is harder to illustrate. But, apparently, of those responses which are equally strongly connected with a situation by nature and equally attended to, some are more susceptible than others to a more intimate connection.

The things which have to be equal in the case of the law of exercise are the force of satisfyingness; that is, the action of the law of effect, and again the readiness of the response to be connected with the situation.

The operation of the laws of instinct, exercise and effect is conditioned further by (1) what may be called the law of assimilation or analogy, — that a situation, especially one to which no particular response is connected by original nature or previous experience, may connect with whatever response is bound to some situation *much like it*, — and (2) by the law of partial activity — that more or less of the total situation may be specially active in determining the response.

The first of these laws is a result of the facts that conduction in the neurones follows the line of least resistance or closest connection, that the action-system is so organized that certain responses tend to be made in their totality if at all, and that slightly different situations may, therefore, produce some one response, the effects of their differences being in the accessories of that response.

The second law is a result of the facts that the situation, itself a compound, produces a compound action in the neurones, and that by reason of inner conditions, the relative intensities of different parts of the compound may vary. The commonest response will be that due to the modal condition of the neural compound, but every condition of the compound will have its response.

THE ADEQUACY OF THE LAWS OF EXERCISE AND EFFECT

Behavior has been supposed to be modified in accordance with three other principles or laws besides the law of exercise and the law of effect. Imitation is often used as a name for the supposed law that the perception of a certain response to a situation by another animal tends in and of itself to connect that response to that situation. Common acceptance has been given to more or less of the law that the idea of an act, or of the result of an act, or of the immediate or remote sensations produced by the act, tends in and of itself to produce the act. Such a law of 'suggestion' or 'ideo-motor' action may be phrased differently, but in whatever form, it insists that the bond between a situation and some conscious representation of a response or of its consequences can do the work of the bond between the situation and the response itself. In acts of reasoning man has been supposed to connect with a given situation a response that could never have been predicted merely from knowledge of what responses were connected with that situation by his original nature or had been connected with it by the laws of exercise and effect. Inference has been supposed to create bonds in and of itself and to be above the mere laws of habit.

Various forms of statement, most of them vague, have been and would be used in describing the potency of a perceived response, a thought-of response, or a train of inference, to produce a response and bind it to the given total situation. Any forms will do for the present argument, since all forms mean to assert that responses can be and often are bound to situations otherwise than by original bodily nature, satisfaction, discomfort, disuse and use. I shall try to show that they cannot; that, on the contrary, the laws of exercise and effect account for all learning.

The facts of imitation in human and animal behavior are explainable by the laws of instinct, exercise and effect.

Some cases of imitation are undoubtedly mere instincts in which the situation responded to is an act by another of the same species. If the baby smiles at a smile, it is because of a special, inborn connection between that sight and that act, — he smiles at a smile for just the same reason that he draws down his mouth and wails at harsh words. At that stage of his life he does not imitate other simple acts. A man runs *with* a crowd for the same reason that he runs *from* a tiger. Returning a blow is no more due to a general tendency to imitate than warding it off is.

Other cases of imitation are mere adjuncts to the ordinary process of habit-formation. In the first place, the act of another, or its result, may serve as a model by which the satisfyingness of one's own responses are determined. Just as the touch and taste of food tells a baby that he has got it safely into his mouth, so the sound of a word spoken by another or the sight of another performing some act of skill tells us whether our pronunciation or technique is right or wrong.

In the second place, the perception of another's act may serve as a stimulus to a response whereby the situation is altered into one to which the animal responds from habit by an act like the one perceived. For example, the perception of another making a certain response (A) to a situation (B) may lead in me by the laws of habit to a response (C) which puts me in a situation (D) such that the response (A) is made by me by the laws of habit. Suppose that by previous training the act of taking off my hat (A) has become connected as response to the situation (D), ' thought of hat off,' and suppose that with the sight of others uncovering their heads (A) in church (B) there has, again by previous habituation, been connected, as response (C), 'thought of hat off.' Then the sight of others uncovering their heads would by virtue of the laws of habit lead me to uncover. Imitation of this sort, where the perception of the act or condition in another gives rise to the idea of performing the act or attaining the condition, the idea in turn giving rise to the appropriate act, is certainly very common.

There may be cases of imitation which cannot be thus accounted for as special instinctive responses to the perception of certain acts by the same acts, as habits formed under the condition that the satisfyingness of a response is its likeness to the perceived act of another, or as the connection of two habits, one of getting, from the perceived act of another, a certain inner condition, the other of getting, from this inner condition, the act in question. There may be, that is, cases where the perceived act of another in and of itself creates a connection.

It is apparently taken for granted by a majority of writers on human behavior that cases of such direct mental infection, as it were, not only exist, but are the rule. I am unable to find proof of such cases, however. Those commonly quoted are far from clear. Learning to talk in the human infant, for example, the stock case of imitation as a direct means of learning, offers only very weak and dubious evidence. Since what is true of it holds substantially for the other favored cases for learning by imitation, I shall examine it at some length.

Let us first be clear as to the alternative explanations of linguistic imitation. The first is that seeing the movements of another's mouth-parts or hearing a series of word-sounds in and of itself produces the response of making that series of sounds or one like it.

The other is that the laws of instinct and habit are adequate to explain the fact in the following manner: A child instinctively produces a great variety of sounds and sound-series. Some of these, accepted as equal to words by the child's companions, are rewarded, so that the child learns by the law of effect to use them in certain situations to attain certain results. It is possible also that a child instinctively feels a special satisfaction at babbling when spoken to and a special satisfaction at finding the sound he makes like one that rings in the ears of memory and has meaning. The latter would be like the instinctive satisfaction apparently felt in constructing an object which is like some real object whose appearance and meaning he knows.

A child also meets frequently the situations 'say dada,' 'say mama,' 'say good night' and the like,[1] and is rewarded when his general babble produces something like the word spoken to him. He thus, by the law of effect, learns to respond to any 'say' situation by making *some* sound and to each of many 'say' situations by making an appropriate sound, and to feel satisfaction at duplicating these words when heard. According to the amount of such training, the tendency to respond to words spoken to him by making some sound may become very strong, and the number of successful duplications very large. Satisfaction may be so connected with saying words that the child practices them by himself orally and even in inner speech. The second alternative relies upon the instinct of babbling, and the satisfaction of getting desirable effects from speech, either the effect which the word has by its meaning as a request ('water,' 'milk,' 'take me outdoors' and the like) or the effect which it has by its mere sound upon companions who notice, pet or otherwise reward a child for linguistic progress.

There are many difficulties in the way of accepting the first alternative. First of all, no one can believe that *all* of a child's speech is acquired by direct imitation. On many occasions the process is undoubtedly one of the production of many sounds, irrespective of the model given, and the selection of the best one by parental reward. Any student who will try to get a child who is just beginning to speak, to say cat, dog and mouse and will record the sounds actually made by the child in the three cases, will find them very much alike. There will in fact be little

[1] The 'say,' may be replaced by some bodily attitude, facial expression, or other verbal formula that identifies the situation as one to be responded to by speech.

that even *looks* like direct imitation until the child has 'learned' at least forty or fifty words.

The second difficulty lies in the fact that different children, in even the clearest cases of the imitation of one sound, vary from it in so many directions. A list of all the sounds made in response to one sound heard is more suggestive of random babble as modified by various habits of duplicating sounds, than of a direct potency of the model. Ten children of the same age may, in response to 'Christmas,' say, kiss, kissus, krismus, mus, kim, kimus, kiruss, i-us and even totally unlike vocables such as hi-yi or ya-ya.

The third difficulty is that in those features of word-sounds which are hard to acquire, such as the 'th' sound, direct imitation is inadequate. The teacher has recourse to trial and chance success, the spoken word serving as a model to guide satisfaction and discomfort. In general no sound not included in the instinctive babble of children seems to be acquired by merely hearing and seeing it made.

A fourth difficulty is that by the doctrine of direct imitation it should not be very much more than two or three times as hard to repeat a two- or three-syllable series as to repeat a single syllable. It is, in fact, enormously harder. This is, of course, just what is to be expected if learning a sound means the selection from random babbling plus previous habits. If, for instance, a child makes thirty monosyllabic sounds like pa, ga, ta, ma, pi, gi, li, mi, etc., there is, by chance, one chance in thirty that in response to a word or phrase he will make that one-syllable sound of his repertory which is most like it, but there is only one chance in nine hundred that he will make that *two-syllable* combination of his repertory which is most like it.

On the other hand, two objections will be made to the opposite view that the word spoken acts only as a model to select from responses otherwise caused, or as a stimulus to habits already existing.   First it will be said that clear, indubitable repetitions of words never practiced by the child, either as totals or in their syllables separately, *do* occur, — that children do respond by repeating a word in cases where full knowledge of all their previous habits would give no reason to expect them to make such a connection.   To this the only retort is that such observations should be based on a very delicate and very elaborate record of a child's linguistic history, and that until they are so made, it is wise to withhold acceptance.

The second objection is that the rapid acquisition of a vocabulary such as occurs in the second and third year is too great a task to be accomplished by the laws of exercise and effect alone.   This objection is based on an overestimation of the variety of sounds which children of the ages in question make.   For example, a child who says 250 words, including say 400 syllables, comprising say 300 syllables which, when properly pronounced, are distinguishable, may actually use less than 50 distinguishable syllables.   *Ba*, may stand for the first syllable of father, water, barn, park and the like.   *Ki* may stand for cry, climb, and even carry. For a child to say a word commonly means that he makes a sound which his intimate companions can recognize as his version of that word.   A child who can produce something like each one of a thousand words upon hearing them, may do so from actual control over less than a hundred syllables.   If we suppose him to have acquired the habits, first, of saying *something* in such a case, second, of responding to a certain hundred sounds when perceived or remembered by making, in each case, a similar sound, and, third, of responding to any other sound when perceived or remembered, by making that sound of his own repertory which is most like it,[1] we can account for a thousand 'imitations,' and still not have made a large demand upon childish powers of learning.

No one should pretend to have disproved direct imitation in the case of learning to talk until he has subjected all these and other matters to crucial experiments. But the burden of proof does seem to belong upon those who deny the adequacy of the laws of exercise and effect. In so far as the choice is between accepting or rejecting a general law that, other things being equal, the perception of a response in another produces that response, we surely must reject it. Some of the cases of imitation may be unexplained by the laws of exercise and effect. But for others no law of imitation is required. And of what should happen by such a law not over a trivial fraction at most does happen.

The idea of a response is in and of itself unable to produce that response.

The early students of behavior, considering human behavior and emphasizing behavior that was thought about and purposive, agreed that the sure way to connect a response with a situation was to choose, or will, or consent to, that response. Later students still agreed that to think about the response in some way, to have an image of it or of the sensations caused in you by previous performances of it, was a strong provocative to it. To get a response, get some sort of conscious representative of it, has been an acceptable maxim. Medicine, education and even advertising have based their practice upon the theory that ideas tended to issue in the particular sort of acts that they were ideas of.

The laws of exercise and effect, on the contrary, if they

---

[1] This would, of course, result from a well-known corollary of the laws of habit.

are the sole laws of modifiability, insist that the thought of an act will produce that act only if the act has been connected with that thought (and without resulting discomfort) in the animal's past.

It seems plausible that there should be a peculiar bond between the thought of a response and the response. The plausibility is due to two reasons, one of which is sound but inadequate, the other being, in my opinion, entirely unsound. The first reason is that, as a mere matter of fact, the thought of a response does so often produce it. The second is that an idea of a response seems a natural and sufficient cause for it to appear. The first reason is inadequate to justify any law of the production of a response by its image or other representative, since evidence can be found to show that when a response is produced by an idea of it, it has been already bound to that idea by repetition or satisfaction. The second reason is unsound because, even if responses are brought to pass occasionally by their images, that is surely an extremely rare and unnatural method.

It is certain that in at least nine cases out of ten a response is produced, not by an image or other representation of it, but by a situation nowise like it or any of its accessories. Hunger and the perception of edible objects, far outweigh ideas of grasping, biting and swallowing, as causes of the eating done in the world. Objects sensed, not images of eye-movements, cause a similar overwhelming majority of the eye's responses. We walk, reach and grasp on most occasions, not because of anticipatory images of how it will feel to do so or verbal descriptions to ourselves of what we are to do, but because we are stimulated by the perception of some object.

It is also certain that the idea of a response may be impotent to produce it. I cannot produce a sneeze by thinking of sneezing. A child may have, in the case of some simple bodily act, which he has done in response to certain situations thousands of times, as adequate ideas of it as are possessed by others, and yet be utterly unable to make himself do it; many adults show this same phenomenon, for instance, in the case of swallowing a pill. And, of course, one can have ideas of running a mile in two minutes, jumping a fence eight feet high, or drawing a line exactly equal to a hundred millimeter line, just as easily as of running the mile in ten minutes, or jumping four feet.

It is further certain that the thought of doing one thing very often results in the man's doing something quite different. The thought of moving the eyes smoothly without stops along a line of print has occurred to many people, who nevertheless actually did as a result move the eyes in a series of jumps with long stops.

It is further certain that in many cases where an animal does connect a given response with the image or thought of that response, the connection has been built up by the laws of exercise and effect. Such cases as appropriate responses to, 'I will go to bed,' 'I will get up,' 'I will eat,' 'I will write a letter,' 'I will read,' or to the corresponding commands, requests or suggestions, are observably built up by training. The appropriate response follows the idea only if it has, by repetition or reward, been connected with it or something like it. If the only requirement in moral education were to have the idea of the right act at the right time, the lives of teachers and parents would be greatly alleviated. But the decision to get up, or the idea of getting up or of being up, is futile until the child has connected therewith the actual act of getting up.

The defender of the direct potency of conscious representatives of a response to produce it may be tempted to complain at this point that what the laws of exercise and effect do is to reduce the strength of competing ideas, and leave the idea, say of getting up, free to exercise its direct potency. The complaint shows a weak sense for fact. The ordinary child is not a Hamlet, nor is he beguiled by the imagined delights of staying in bed, nor repelled by the image of getting up out of it. On the contrary, he may be entirely willing to *think of* getting up. It is the actual delights that hold him, the actual discomforts that check him, and the only way to be sure that he will get up is so to arrange matters that it is more satisfactory to him to get up than not to when the situation, whatever it be, that is to suggest that response, makes its appearance.

The experience of every schoolroom shows that it is not enough to get the idea of an act. The act must have gone with that idea or be now put with it. The bond must be created. Responses to the suggestions of language, whether addressed to us by others or by ourselves in inner speech, in a very large majority of cases owe their bonds to the laws of exercise and effect. We learn to do what we are told, or what we tell ourselves, by doing *something* and rejecting or retaining what we do by virtue of its effects. So also in the case of a majority of responses to the suggestions of other than verbal imagery.

The idea of a response, like the perception of a response by another, acts often as a guide to response *ex post facto* by deciding what shall be satisfying. Where superficial inspection leaves the impression that the idea creates the act, a little care often shows it to have only selected from the acts produced by instinct and habit. For example, let the reader think of some act never performed hitherto, such as putting his left middle finger upon the upper right hand corner of this page, and make the movement. It may seem at first sight that having the idea entirely unopposed was the sufficient cause of the act. But careful experiment, including, for instance, the closure of the eyes and anesthesia of the fingers will reveal that the original propulsion of the idea is not to just that act, but to many possibilities, and that its chief potency lies in the fact that not to get the finger to that point is annoying, and that consequently the organism is at peace only when the act is done.

So far it has been shown that: The majority of responses are not produced by ideas of them. The idea of a response may be impotent to produce it. The idea of one act may produce a different, even an opposite act. When an idea seems to produce a response in and of itself, it may really act by determining the satisfyingness of responses otherwise made. These facts are sufficient to destroy the pretensions of any general law that the image of an act will, other things being equal, produce it. But the possibility that such an image may occasionally exercise this peculiar potency remains.

I despair of convincing the reader that it does not. Man is the only animal possessing a large fund of ideas of acts, and man's connection-system is so complex and his ideas of acts are so intricately bound to situations that have by use and effect produced those acts, that the proof of this negative is a practical impossibility. But it is possible to show that even the most favored cases for the production of a response by securing an ideal representation of it may be explainable by use and effect alone.

The extreme apparent potency of ideas representing acts to produce them regardless of bonds of use or effect is, of course, witnessed in the phenomena of suggestion in hypnosis and allied states. To try to reduce these phenomena to consequences of the laws of habit may seem fanatical. Here, it will be said, are the crucial cases where the idea of an act, if freed from all effects of opposing ideas, does inevitably produce the act so far as it is a possibility for the animal's action-system.

That is precisely what I cannot find proof of.

Efficient suggestions to hypnotized subjects, on the contrary, are often ambiguous in the sense that they seem as likely to arouse a situation *to which the act has been bound by the law of habit* as to arouse an idea of the act. Often they are far better suited to the former purpose. Direct commands — Walk, Dance, Get up, Sit down — obviously will operate by the law of habit provided the situations connected with disobedience are excluded. This is also the case with such indirect suggestions as 'This is a knife (stick).' 'This is your sword (broom).' 'Have a cigar (a pen).'

The release of a suggestion from inhibitions may as well be the release from *ideas connected as antecedents with* not performing the act as the release from *ideas of* not performing it. It is a question of fact whether, to get an act done by the subject, one must arouse in him an idea to which or to a part of which or to something like which the act has been bound by use or effect, or may arouse simply an idea of the act.

Finally, if an idea has a tendency to connect with a certain response, over and above the bonds due to exercise and effect, it should *always* manifest that tendency. If the connection is not made, it must be due to the action of some contrary force. It is less my duty to show that the laws of habit can account for hypnotic suggestibility, obsessions, and the like, than it is my opponents' duty to explain why a man can spend a half day in hospitably welcoming a hundred ideas of acts and yet perform no one of them, save those in the case of which he has learned to do the thing when he thinks of doing it. Again, how can the mere addition of the idea of a future date to the idea of an act so utterly deprive it of present potency.

In view of all these facts it seems probable that ideas of responses act in connection just as do any other situations, and that the phenomena of suggestion and ideo-motor action really mean that any idea will, except for competing ideas, produce the response, not that *is like it*, but that *has gone with it*, or with some idea like it.

Rational connections are, in their causation, like any others, the difference being in what is connected.

It remains to ask whether situation and response are bound together in the case of reasoning by any other forces than the forces of repetition, energy and satisfaction? Do the laws of inferential thinking transcend the laws of exercise and effect? Or does the mind, even in these novel and constructive responses, do only what it is forced to do by original nature or has done without discomfort?

To defend the second alternative involves the reduction of the processes of abstraction, association by similarity and selective thinking to mere secondary consequences of the laws of exercise and effect. This I shall try to do.

The gist of the fact of abstraction is that response may be made to some elements or aspects of a situation which have never been experienced in isolation, and may be made to the element in question regardless of the gross total situation in which it inheres. A baby thus learns to respond to its mother's face regardless of what total visual field it is a part of. A child thus learns to respond by picking out any red object, regardless of whether the redness be in an apple, a block, a pencil, a ribbon or a ball. A student thus learns to respond to any plane surface inclosed by three straight lines regardless of its size, shape, color or other than geometrical meaning.

What happens in such cases is that the response, by being connected with many situations alike in the presence of the element in question and different in other respects, is bound firmly to that element and loosely to each of its concomitants. Conversely any element is bound firmly to any one response that is made to all situations containing it and very, very loosely to each of those responses that are made to only a few of the situations containing it. The element of triangularity, for example, is bound firmly to the response of saying or thinking 'triangle' but only very loosely to the response of saying or thinking white, red, blue, large, small, iron, steel, wood, paper and the like. A situation thus acquires bonds not only with some response to it as a gross total, but also with responses to each of its elements that has appeared in any other gross totals.

Appropriate response to an element regardless of its concomitants is a necessary consequence of the laws of exercise and effect if an animal learns to make that response to the gross total situations that contain the element and not to make it to those that do not. Such prepotent determination of the response by one or another element of the situation is no transcendental mystery, but, given the circumstances, a general rule of all learning. The dog who responds appropriately to 'beg' no matter when, where, or by whom spoken, manifests the same laws of behavior. There is no difficulty in understanding how each element of a situation may come to tend to produce a response peculiar to it as well as to play its part in determining the response to the situation as a total. There may be some difficulty in understanding how each element of a situation comes to be *felt* whereas before only the gross total was felt.   The change in consciousness from the 'big, blooming, buzzing confusion' to an aggregate of well-defined percepts and images, which accompanies the change in behavior from response to totals to response to parts or elements, may be mysterious.   With the change in consciousness, however, we are not now concerned.   The *behavior* of man and other animals toward the abstract elements of color, size, number, form, time or value is explained by the laws of instinct, exercise and effect.

When the perception or thought of a fact arouses the thought of some other fact identical in part with the former fact, we have so-called association by similarity.   An element of the neurone-action is prepotent in determining the succeeding neurone-action.   The particular way in which it determines it is by itself continuing and making connection with other associates.   These it possesses by virtue of the law of exercise and effect.

The changes in behavior classified under intellect and morality seem then to be all explainable by the two laws of exercise and effect.   The facts of imitation really refer to certain specific original connections or to the efficiency of a model in determining what shall satisfy or to the provision of certain instructive situations in the form of the behavior of other animals.   The facts variously referred to as suggestion, ideo-motor action or the motor power of ideas, really refer to the fact, common in the human animal only, that to those ideas that represent acts in thought the acts are often bound as responses.   The bonds are due to the primary laws of effect and exercise.   The facts of reasoning really refer to the fact of prepotency of one or another element in a situation in determining the response.

The reduction of all learning to making and rewarding or avoiding and punishing connections between situation and response allows changes in intellect and character to be explained by changes in the neurones that are known either to be or to be possible. I have elsewhere sketched one such possible neural mechanism for the law of effect.[1]

On the contrary, imitation, suggestion and reasoning, as commonly described, put an intolerable burden upon the neurones. To any one who has tried to imagine a possible action in the neurones to parallel the traditional power of the mere perception of an act in another or of the mere representation of an act as done by oneself to produce that act, this is a great merit. For the only adequate psychological parallel of traditional imitation and suggestion would be the original existence or the gratuitous formation of a connection between (1) each neurone-action corresponding to a percept of an act done by another or to the idea of an act done by oneself and (2) the neurone-action arousing that act. It is incredible that the neurone-action corresponding to the perception of a response in another, or to the idea of a response in oneself, or to the first term in an association by similarity, should have, in and of itself, a special power to determine that the next neurone-action should be that paralleling the response in question. And there is no possible physiological parallel of a power to jump from premise to conclusion for no other reason than the ideal fitness of the sequence.

SIMPLIFICATIONS OF THE LAWS OF EXERCISE AND EFFECT

There has been one notable attempt to explain the facts of learning by an even simpler theory than that represented

---

[1] In *Essays Philosophical and Psychological in Honor of William James*, pp. 591–599.

in the laws of exercise and effect. Jennings has formulated as an adequate account of learning the law that: "When a certain physiological state has been resolved, through the continued action of an external agent, or otherwise, into a second physiological state, this resolution becomes easier, so that in course of time it takes place quickly and spontaneously" ('Behavior of the Lower Organisms,' p. 289). "The law may be expressed briefly as follows: — *The resolution of one physiological state into another becomes easier and more rapid after it has taken place a number of times.* Hence the behavior primarily characteristic for the second state comes to follow immediately upon the first state. The operations of this law are, of course, seen on a vast scale in higher organisms in the phenomena which we commonly call memory, association, habit formation and learning" (*ibid.*, p. 291). This law may be expressed conveniently as a tendency of a series of states

$$A \to B \to C \to D$$

to become $\qquad A \to D$

or $\qquad A \to B^1 \to C^1 \to D$

B^1 and C^1 being states B and C passed rapidly and in a modified way so that they do not result in a reaction but are resolved directly into D.

If Professor Jennings had applied to this law the same rigorous analysis which he has so successfully employed elsewhere, he would have found that it could be potent to cause learning only if supplemented by the law of effect and then only for a fraction of learning.

For, the situations being the same, the state A cannot produce, at one time, now B and, at another time, abbreviated, rudimentary B^1 instead of B. If A with S produces B once, it must always. If D or a rudimentary B^1 is produced, there must be something other than A; A must itself have

changed. Something must have been added to or subtracted from it. In Professor Jennings' own words, "Since
the external conditions have not changed, the animal itself must have changed" (*ibid.*, p. 286). And in adaptive
learning something related to the results of the S A connection must have changed it.

The series A — B — C — D does not become the series
A — D or A — B^1 — C^1 — D by magic. If B and C are
weakened and D is strengthened as sequents of A in response to S, it is because something other than repetition
acts upon them. Repetition alone could not blow hot
for D and cold for B.

Moreover, as a mere matter of fact, "the resolution of one
physiological state into another" through intermediate
states does not with enough repetition "become easier so
that in course of time it takes place quickly and spontaneously."

Paramecium does not change its response to, say, an obstacle in the water, from swimming backward, turning to
one side and swimming forward by abbreviating and eventually omitting the turn and the backward movement.
The schoolboy does not tend to count 1, 2, 10 or to say
a, b, z, or give ablative plurals after nominative singulars.

Repetition of a series of physiological states in and of itself on the contrary makes an animal increasingly *more*
likely to *maintain* the series *in toto*. It is hard to give the
first and then the last word of an oft repeated passage like
Hamlet's soliloquy or the Lord's Prayer, or to make readily
the first and then the last movement of writing a name or
address. Repetition never eliminates absolutely and eliminates relatively the *less* often or *less* emphatically connected.

Even if supplemented by the law of effect, so that some
force is at hand to change the effect of S upon the animal

to A D instead of the original A B C D, the law of the resolution of physiological states would be relevant to only a fraction of learning. For example, let a cat or dog be given an ordinary discrimination experiment, but so modified that whether the animal responds by the 'right' or the 'wrong' act *he is removed immediately after the reward or punishment.* That is, the event is either S R_1 or S R_2, *never* S R_1 R_2. Let the experiment be repeated at intervals so long that the physiological state, St. R_1, or St. R_2, leading to the response R_1 or R_2 in the last trial, has ceased before the next. The animal will come to respond to S by R_2 only, though R_2 has never been reached by the 'resolution' of S R_1 R_2.

Cats in jumping for birds or mice, men in playing billiards, tennis or golf, and many other animals in many other kinds of behavior, often learn as the dog must in this experiment. The situation on different occasions is followed by different responses, but by only one per occasion. Professor Jennings was misled by treating as general the special case where the situation itself includes a condition of discomfort terminable only by a 'successful' response or by the animal's exhaustion or death.

Assuming as typical this same limited case of response to an annoying situation, so that success consists simply in replacing the situation by another, Stevenson Smith reduces the learning-process to the law of exercise alone. He argues that, —

"For instance, let an organism at birth be capable of giving N reactions (a, b, c, . . . N) to a definite stimulus S and let only one of these reactions be appropriate. If only one reaction can be given at a time and if the one given is determined by the state of the organism at the time S is received, there is one chance in N that it is the appropriate reaction. When the appropriate reaction is finally given, the other reactions are not called into play, S may cease to act, but until the appropriate reaction is given let the organism be such that it runs through the gamut of the others until the appropriate reaction is brought about. As there are N possible reactions, the chances are that the appropriate reaction will be given before all N are performed. At the next appearance of the stimulus, which we may call S_2, those reactions which were in the last case performed, are, through habit, more likely to be again brought about than those which were not performed. Let u stand for the unperformed reactions. Then we have $N - u$ probable reactions to S_2. Habit rendering the previously most performed reactions the most probable throughout we should expect to find the appropriate reaction in response to

S_1 contained in N.

S_2 contained in $N - u_1$.

S_3 contained in $N - u_1 - u_2$.

. . . .

S_n contained in $N - nu$, which approaches *one* as a limit.

ı Thus the appropriate reaction would be fixed through the laws of chance and habit. This law of habit is that when any action is performed a number of times under certain conditions, it becomes under those conditions more and more easily performed" (*Journal of Comparative Neurology and Psychology*, 1908, Vol. XVIII, pp. 503–504).

This hypothesis is, like Professor Jennings', adequate to account for only the one special case, and is adequate to account for that only upon a further limitation of the number of times that the animal may repeat any one of his varied responses to the situation before he has gone through them all once, or reached the one that puts an end to the situation.

The second limitation may be illustrated in the simple hypothetical case of three responses, 1, 2 and 3, of which No. 2 is successful. Suppose the animal always to go through his repertory with *no* repetitions until he reaches 2 and so closes the series.

Only the following can happen : —

$$1\ 2$$
$$1\ 3\ 2$$
$$2$$
$$2$$
$$3\ 1\ 2$$
$$3\ 2$$

and, in the long run, 2 will happen twice as often as 1 or 3 happens.

Suppose the animal to repeat each response of his repertory six times before changing to another, the remaining conditions being as above. Then only the following can happen : —

$$1\ 1\ 1\ 1\ 1\ 1\ 2$$
$$1\ 1\ 1\ 1\ 1\ 1\ 3\ 3\ 3\ 3\ 3\ 3\ 2$$
$$2$$
$$2$$
$$3\ 3\ 3\ 3\ 3\ 3\ 1\ 1\ 1\ 1\ 1\ 1\ 2$$
$$3\ 3\ 3\ 3\ 3\ 3\ 2,$$

and in the long run 2 will happen one third as often as 1 or 3 and, though always successful, must, by Smith's theory, appear later and later, so that if the animal meets the situation often enough, he will eventually fail utterly in it !

Animals do, as a matter of fact, commonly repeat responses many times before changing them,[1] so that if only the law

[1] Professor Smith's own experiments illustrate this.

of exercise operated, learning would not be adaptive. It is
the *effect* of 2 that gives it the advantage over 1 and 3. Of
two responses to the same annoying situation, one continuing and the other relieving it, an animal could never learn
to adopt the latter as a result of the law of exercise alone,
if the former was, originally, twice as likely to occur.　1 1 2
would occur as often as 2 and exercise would be equal for
both. The convincing cases are, of course, those where
learning equals the strengthening to supremacy of an
originally very weak connection and the weakening of
originally strong bonds. An animal's original nature may
lead it to behave as shown below: —

1 1 3 1 1 4 1 1 2

1 1 1 3 1 1 1 3 1 1 4 2

4 1 1 3 3 1 1 4 4 1 1 1 1 1 2, etc.,

and yet the animal's eventual behavior may be to react to
the situation always by 2. The law of effect is primary,
irreducible to the law of exercise.

THE EVOLUTION OF BEHAVIOR

The acceptance of the laws of exercise and effect as adequate accounts of learning would make notable differences
in the treatment of all problems that concern learning. I
shall take, to illustrate this, the problem of the development
of intellect and character in the animal series, the phylogenesis of intellectual and moral behavior.

The difficulties in the way of understanding the evolution
of intellectual and moral behavior have been that neither
what had been evolved nor that from which it had been
evolved was understood.

The behavior of the higher animals, especially man, was
thought to be a product of impulses and ideas which got

into the mind in various ways and had power to arouse certain acts and other ideas more or less mysteriously, in the manner described by the laws of ideo-motor action, attention, association by contiguity, association by similarity, suggestion, imitation, dynamo-genesis and the like, with possibly a surplus of acts and ideas due to 'free will.' The mind was treated as a crucible in which a multifarious solution of ideas, impulses and automatisms boiled away, giving off, as a consequence of a subtle chemistry, an abundance of thoughts and movements. Human behavior was rarely viewed from without as a series of responses bound in various ways to a series of situations. The student of animal behavior passed as quickly as might be from such mere externals to the inner life of the creature, making it his chief interest to decide whether it had percepts, memories, concepts, abstractions, ideas of right and wrong, choices, a self, a conscience, a sense of beauty. The facts in intellect and character that are due to learning, that are not the inherited property of the species and that consequently are beyond the scope of evolution in the race, were not separated off from the facts of original nature. The comparative psychologist misspent his energy on such problems as the phylogenesis of the idea of self, moral judgments, or the sentiment of filial affection.

At the other extreme, the behavior of the protozoa was either contemplated in the light of futile analogies, — for instance, between discriminative reactions and conscious choice, and between inherited instincts and memory, — or studied crudely in its results without observation of what the animals really did. The protozoa were regarded either as potential 'conscious selves' or as drifting lumps turned hither and thither by the direct effects of light, heat, gravity and chemical forces upon their tissues.

The evolution of the intellectual and moral nature which a higher animal really possesses from the sort of a nature which the real activities of the protozoa manifest, is far less difficult to explain.

In so far as the higher animal is a collection of original tendencies to respond to physical events without and within the body, subject to modification by the laws of exercise and effect and by these alone, and in so far as the protozoan is already possessed of a well-defined repertory of responses connected with physical events without and within the body in substantially the manner of the higher animal's original tendencies, the problems of the evolution of behavior are definite and in the way of solution.

The previous sections gave reason for the belief that the higher animals, including man, manifest no behavior beyond expectation from the laws of instinct, exercise and effect. The human mind was seen to do no more than connect in accord with original bonds, use and disuse, and the satisfaction and discomfort resulting to the neurones. The work of Jennings has shown that the protozoa already possess full-fledged instincts, homologous with the instincts of man. They too may have specialized receptors, an action-system with a well-defined repertory and a connecting system or means of influencing the bonds between the stimuli received and the motor reactions made. The difficulties of tracing the possible development of a super-man from an infra-animal thus disappear.

There is, of course, an abundance of *bona fide* difficulty in discovering the unlearned behavior of each group of animals and in tracing, throughout the animal series, changes in the physical events to which animals are sensitive so that to each a different response may be attached, changes in the movements of which animals are capable, and changes in the bonds by which particular movements follow particular physical events. To find when and how animals whose natures remained nearly or quite unchanged by the satisfying and annoying effects of their behavior, gave birth to animals that could learn, is perhaps a still harder task. But these tasks concern problems that are intelligible matters of fact. They do not require a student to get out of matter something defined as beyond matter, or to get volition out of tropisms, or to get ideas of space and time out of swimming and sleeping.

The evolution of the sensitivities and of the action-systems of animals has already been subjected to matter-of-fact study by naturalists. The evolution of the connection-system will soon be. Each reflex, instinct or capacity, each bond between a given situation presented to a given physiological state and a given response, has its an-cestral tree. Scratching at an irritated spot on the skin is older than arms. Following an object that is moving slowly does not have to be explained separately, as a 'chance' variation in dogs, sheep and babies. The me-chanical trades of man are related to the miscellaneous manipulations of the apes. Little as we know of the con-nection-systems possessed by animals, we know enough to be sure that a bond between situation and response has ancestors and children as truly as does any bodily organ. Professor Whitman a decade ago showed the pos-sibility of phylogenetic investigation of instinctive con-nections in a study which should be a stimulus and model for many others. In place of any further general account of the study of the phylogeny of the connection-system, I shall quote from his account of the concrete phylogeny of the instinct of incubation.

"*b. The Incubation Instinct*

1. *Meaning to be Sought in Phyletic Roots.* — It seems quite natural to think of incubation merely as a means of providing the heat needed for the development of the egg, and to assume that the need was felt before the means was found to meet it.   Birds and eggs are thus presupposed, and as the birds could not have foreseen the need, they could not have hit upon the means except by accident. Then, what an infinite amount of chancing must have followed before the first 'cuddling' became a habit, and the habit a perfect instinct!   We are driven to such preposterous extremities as the result of taking a purely casual feature to start with.   Incubation supplies the needed heat, but that is an incidental utility that has nothing to do with the nature and origin of the instinct.   It enables us to see how natural selection has added some minor adjustments, but explains nothing more.   For the real meaning of the instinct we must look to its phyletic roots.

If we go back to animals standing near the remote ancestors of birds, to the amphibia and fishes, we find the same instinct stripped of its later disguises.   Here one or both parents simply remain over or near the eggs and keep a watchful guard against enemies.   Sometimes the movements of the parent serve to keep the eggs supplied with fresh water, but aëration is not the purpose for which the instinct exists.

2. *Means Rest and Incidental Protection to Offspring.* — The instinct is a part of the reproductive cycle of activities, and always holds the same relation in all forms that exhibit it, whether high or low.   It follows the production of eggs, or young, and means primarily, as I believe, rest, with

incidental protection to offspring. That meaning is always manifest, no less in worms, molluscs, crustacea, spiders and insects, than in fishes, amphibia, reptiles and birds. The instinct makes no distinction between eggs and young, and that is true all along the line up to birds, which extend the same blind instinct to one as to the other.

3. *Essential Elements of the Instinct.* — Every essential element in the instinct of incubation was present long before the birds and eggs arrived. These elements are: (1) the disposition to remain with or over the eggs; (2) the disposition to resist and drive away enemies; and (3) periodicity. The birds brought all these elements along in their congenital equipment, and added a few minor adaptations, such as cutting the period of incubation to the need of normal development, and thus avoiding indefinite waste of time in case of sterile or abortive eggs.

(1) *Disposition to Remain over the Eggs.* — The disposition to remain over the eggs is certainly very old, and is probably bound up with the physiological necessity for rest after a series of activities tending to exhaust the whole system. If this suggestion seems far-fetched, when thinking of birds, it will seem less so as we go back to simpler conditions, as we find them among some of the lower invertebrate forms, which are relatively very inactive and predisposed to remain quiet until impelled by hunger to move. Here we find animals remaining over their eggs, and thus shielding them from harm, from sheer inability or indisposition to move. That is the case with certain molluscs (*Crepidula*), the habits and development of which have been recently studied by Professor Conklin. Here full protection to offspring is afforded without any exertion on the part of the parent, in a strictly passive way that excludes even any instinctive care. In *Clepsine* there is a manifest un-

willingness to leave the eggs, showing that the disposition to remain over them is instinctive. If we start with forms of similar sedentary mode of life, it is easy to see that remaining over the eggs would be the most likely thing to happen, even if no instinctive regard for them existed. The protection afforded would, however, be quite sufficient to insure the development of the instinct, natural selection favoring those individuals which kept their position unchanged long enough for the eggs to hatch." [1]

Professor Whitman proceeds to study the ' Disposition to Resist Enemies ' and the ' Periodicity ' in the same genetic way.

The most important of all original abilities is the ability to learn. It, like other capacities, has evolved. The animal series shows a development from animals whose connection-system suffers little or no permanent modification by experience to animals whose connections are in large measure created by use and disuse, satisfaction and discomfort.

Some of this development can be explained without recourse to differences in mere power to learn, by the fact that the latter animals are given greater stimuli to or rewards for learning. But part of it is due to differences in sheer ability to learn, that is, in the power of equally satisfying conditions to strengthen or of equally annoying conditions to weaken bonds in the animals' connection-systems. This may be seen from the following simple and partial case: —

Call 1 and 2 two animals.

Call C_1 and C_2 the internal conditions of the two animals

---

[1] Biological Lectures from the Marine Biological Laboratory of Woods Holl, 1898, p. 323 ff.

except for their connection-systems, each being the average condition of the animal in question.

Call S_1 and S_2 two external states of affairs, each being near the indifference point for the animal in question, — that is, being one which the animal does little to either avoid or secure.

Call G_1 and G_2 two responses which result in O_1 and O_2 the *optima* or most satisfying state of affairs for 1 and 2.

Call I_1 and I_2 two responses which result in the continuation of S_1 and S_2.

The only responses possible for 1 are G_1 and I_1.

The only responses possible for 2 are G_2 and I_2.

Animal 1 upon the recurrence of S_1 and C_1 is little or no more likely to respond by G_1 than he was before.

Animal 2 upon the recurrence of S_2 and C_2 is far more likely to respond by G_2 than he was before.

The fact thus outlined might conceivably be due to an intrinsic inequality between O_1 and O_2, the power of equally satisfying *optima* to influence, their antecedents being identical. This is not the case in the evolution of learning, however. For even if, instead of O_2, we had only a moderately satisfying state of affairs, such as the company of other chicks to (2) a 15-day-old chick, while O_1 was the optimum of darkness, dampness, coolness, etc., for (1) an earthworm, 2 would learn far, far more rapidly than 1.

The fact is due, of course, to the unequal power of equally satisfying conditions to influence their antecedents. The same argument holds good for the influence of discomfort.

The ability to learn, — that is, the possession of a connection-system subject to the laws of exercise and effect, — has been found in animals as 'low' as the starfish and perhaps in the protozoa. It is hard to tell whether the changed responses observed in Stentor by Jennings and in

Paramecium by Stevenson Smith are easily forgotten learnings or long retained excitabilities. Sooner or later clear learning appears, and then, from crabs to fish and turtle, from these to various birds and mammals, from these to monkeys, and from these to man, a fairly certain increase in sheer ability to learn, in the potency of a supposedly constant degree of satisfyingness or annoyingness to influence the connection preceding it, can be assumed. We cannot, of course, define just what we mean by equal satisfyingness to a mouse and a man, but the argument is substantially the same as that whereby we assume that the gifted boy has more sheer ability to learn than the idiot, so that if the two made the same response to the same situation and were equally satisfied thereby, the former would form the habit more firmly.

We may, therefore, expect that when knowledge of the structure and behavior of the neurones comprising the connection-systems of animals (or of the neurones' predecessors in this function) progresses far enough to inform us of just what happens when a connection is made stronger or weaker and of just what effects satisfying and annoying states of affairs exert upon the connection-system (and in particular upon the connections most recently in activity) the ability to learn will show as true an evolution as the ability to sneeze, oppose the thumb, or clasp an object touched by the hand.

If my analysis is true, the evolution of behavior is a rather simple matter. Formally the crab, fish, turtle, dog, cat, monkey and baby have very similar intellects and characters. All are systems of connections subject to change by the law of exercise and effect. The differences are: first, in the concrete particular connections, in *what* stimulates the animal to response, *what* responses it makes, *which* stimulus connects with *which* response, and second, in the degree of ability to learn — in the amount of influence of a given degree of satisfyingness or annoyingness upon the connection that produced it.

The peculiarly human features of intellect and character, responses to elements and symbols, are the results of: first, a receiving system that is easily stimulated by the external world bit by bit (as by focalized vision and touch with the moving hand) as well as in totals composed of various aggregates of these bits; second, of an action-system of great versatility (as in facial expression, articulation, and the hands' movements); and third, of a connection-system that includes the connections roughly denoted by babbling, manipulation, curiosity, and satisfaction at activity, bodily or mental, for its own sake; that is capable of working in great detail, singling out elements of situations and parts of responses; and that allows satisfying and annoying states of affairs to exert great influence on their antecedent connections. Because he learns fast and learns much, in the animal way, man seems to learn by intuitions of his own.

CHAPTER VII

The Evolution of the Human Intellect[1]

To the intelligent man with an interest in human nature it must often appear strange that so much of the energy of the scientific world has been spent on the study of the body and so little on the study of the mind. 'The greatest thing in man is mind,' he might say, 'yet the least studied.' Especially remarkable seems the rarity of efforts to trace the evolution of the human intellect from that of the lower animals. Since Darwin's discovery, the beasts of the field, the fowl of the air and the fish of the sea have been examined with infinite pains by hundreds of workers in the effort to trace our physical genealogy, and with consummate success; yet few and far between have been the efforts to find the origins of intellect and trace its progress up to human faculty. And none of them has achieved any secure success.

It may be premature to try again, but a somewhat extended series of studies of the intelligent behavior of fishes, reptiles, birds and mammals, including the monkeys, which it has been my lot to carry out during the last five years, has brought results which seem to throw light on the problem and to suggest its solution.

Experiments have been made on fishes, reptiles, birds and various mammals, notably dogs, cats, mice and monkeys, to see how they learned to do certain simple things in order

[1] This chapter appeared originally in the *Popular Science Monthly*, Nov., 1901.

to get food. All these animals manifest fundamentally the same sort of intellectual life. Their learning is after the same general type. What that type is can be seen best from a concrete instance. A monkey was kept in a large cage. Into the cage was put a box, the door of which was held closed by a wire fastened to a nail which was inserted in a hole in the top of the box. If the nail was pulled up out of the hole, the door could be pulled open. In this box was a piece of banana. The monkey, attracted by the new object, came down from the top of the cage and fussed over the box. He pulled at the wire, at the door, and at the bars in the front of the box. He pushed the box about and tipped it up and down. He played with the nail and finally pulled it out. When he happened to pull the door again, of course it opened. He reached in and got the food inside. It had taken him 36 minutes to get in. Another piece of food being put in and the door closed, the occurrences of the first trial were repeated, but there was less of the profitless pulling and tipping. He got in this time in 2 minutes and 20 seconds. With repeated trials the animal finally came to drop entirely the profitless acts and to take the nail out and open the door as soon as the box was put in his cage. He had, we should say, learned to get in.

The process involved in the learning was evidently a process of selection. The animal is confronted by a state of affairs or, as we may call it, a 'situation.' He reacts in the way that he is moved by his innate nature or previous training to do, by a number of acts. These acts include the particular act that is appropriate and he succeeds. In later trials the impulse to this one act is more and more stamped in, this one act is more and more associated with that situation, is selected from amongst the others by reason of the pleasure it brings the animal. The profitless acts are stamped out; the impulses to perform them in that situation are weakened by reason of the positive discomfort or the absence of pleasure resulting from them. So the animal finally performs in that situation only the fitting act.

Here we have the simplest and at the same time the most widespread sort of intellect or learning in the world. There is no reasoning, no process of inference or comparison; there is no thinking about things, no putting two and two together; there are no ideas — the animal does not think of the box or of the food or of the act he is to perform. He simply comes after the learning to feel like doing a certain thing under certain circumstances which before the learning he did not feel like doing. Human beings are accustomed to think of intellect as the power of having and controlling ideas and of ability to learn as synonymous with ability to have ideas. But learning by having ideas is really one of the rare and isolated events in nature. There may be a few scattered ideas possessed by the higher animals, but the common form of intelligence with them, their habitual method of learning, is not by the acquisition of ideas, but by the selection of impulses.

Indeed this same type of learning is found in man. When we learn to drive a golf ball or play tennis or billiards, when we learn to tell the price of tea by tasting it or to strike a certain note exactly with the voice, we do not learn in the main by virtue of any ideas that are explained to us, by any inferences that we reason out. We learn by the gradual selection of the appropriate act or judgment, by its association with the circumstances or situation requiring it, in just the way that the animals do.

From the lowest animals of which we can affirm intelligence up to man this type of intellect is found. With it there are in the mammals obscure traces of the ideas which come in the mental life of man to outweigh and hide it. But it is the basal fact. As we follow the development of animals in time, we find the capacity to select impulses growing. We find the associations thus made between situation and act growing in number, being formed more quickly, lasting longer and becoming more complex and more delicate. The fish can learn to go to certain places, to take certain paths, to bite at certain things and refuse others, but not much more. It is an arduous proceeding for him to learn to get out of a small pen by swimming up through a hole in a screen. The monkey can learn to do all sorts of things. It is a comparatively short and easy task for him to learn to get into a box by unhooking a hook, pushing a bar around and pulling out a plug. He learns quickly to climb down to a certain place when he sees a letter T on a card and to stay still when he sees a K. He performs the proper acts nearly as well after 50 days as he did when they were fresh in his mind.

This growth in the number, speed of formation, permanence, delicacy and complexity of associations possible for an animal reaches its acme in the case of man. Even if we leave out of question the power of reasoning, the possession of a multitude of ideas and abstractions and the power of control over impulses, purposive action, man is still the intellectual leader of the animal kingdom by virtue of the superior development in him of the power of forming associations between situations or sense-impressions and acts, by virtue of the degree to which the mere learning by selection possessed by all intelligent animals has advanced. In man the type of intellect common to the animal kingdom finds its fullest development, and with it is combined the hitherto nonexistent power of thinking about things and rationally directing action in accord with thought.

Indeed it may be that this very reason, self-consciousness and self-control which seem to sever human intellect so sharply from that of all other animals are really but secondary results of the tremendous increase in the number, delicacy and complexity of associations which the human animal can form.   It may be that the evolution of intellect has no breaks, that its progress is continuous from its first appearance to its present condition in adult civilized human beings.   If we could prove that what we call ideational life and reasoning were not new and unexplainable species of intellectual life but only the natural consequences of an increase in the number, delicacy, and complexity of associations of the general animal sort, we should have made out an evolution of mind comparable to the evolution of living forms.

In 1890 William James wrote, "The more sincerely one seeks to trace the actual course of psychogenesis, the steps by which as a race we may have come by the peculiar mental attributes which we possess, the more clearly one perceives 'the slowly gathering twilight close in utter dark.'"   Can we perhaps prove him a false prophet?   Let us first see if there be any evidence that makes it probable that in some way or another the mere extension of the animal type of intellect has produced the human sort.   If we do, let us proceed to seek a possible account of *how* this might have happened, and finally to examine any evidence that shows this possible 'how' to have been the real way in which human reason has evolved.

It has already been shown that in the animal kingdom there is, as we pass from the early vertebrates down to man, a progress in the evolution of the general associative process which practically equals animal intellect, that this progress continues as we pass from the monkeys to man.   Such a progress is a real fact; it does exist as a possible *vera causa;* it is thus at all events better than some imaginary cause of the origin of human intellect, the very existence of which is in doubt. In a similar manner we know that the neurones, which compose the brain and the connections between which are the physiological parallels of the habits that animals form, show, as we pass down through the vertebrate series, an evolution along lines of increased delicacy and complexity. That an animal associates a certain act with a certain felt situation means that he forms or strengthens connections between certain cells. The increase in number, delicacy and complexity of cell structures is thus the basis for an increase in the number, delicacy and complexity of associations. Now the evolution noted in cell structures affects man as well as the other vertebrates. He stands at the head of the scale in that respect as well. May not this obvious supremacy in the animal type of intellect and in the adaption of his brain to it be at the bottom of his supremacy in being the sole possessor of reasoning?

This question becomes more pressing if we realize that we must have some sort of brain correlate for ideational life and reasoning. Some sort of difference in processes in the brain must be at the basis of the mental differences between man and the lower animals, we should all admit. And it would seem wise to look for that difference amongst differences which really do or at least may exist. Now the most likely brain difference between man and the lower animals for our purpose, to my mind indeed the only likely one, is just this difference in the fineness of organization of the cell structures. If we could show with any degree of probability how it might account for the presence of ideas and of reasoning, we should at least have the satisfaction of dealing with a cause actually known to exist.

The next important fact is that the intellect of the infant six months to a year old is of the animal sort, that ideational and reasoning life are not present in his case, that the only obvious intellectual difference between him and a monkey is in the quantity and quality of the associations formed. In the evolution of the infant's mind to its adult condition we have the actual transition within an individual from the animal to the human type of intellect. If we look at the infant and ask what is in him to make in the future a thinker and reasoner, we must answer either by invoking some mysterious capacity, the presence of which we cannot demonstrate, or by taking the difference we actually do find. That is the difference in the quality and quantity of associations of the animal sort. Even if we could never see how it came to cause the future intellectual life, it would seem wiser to believe that it did than to resort to faith in mysteries. Surely there is enough evidence to make it worth while to ask our second question, "How might this difference cause the life of ideas and reasoning?"

To answer this question fully would involve a most intricate treatment of the whole intellectual life of man, a treatment which cannot be attempted without reliance on technical terms and psychological formulas. A fairly comprehensible account of the general features of such an answer can, however, be given. The essential thing about the thinking of the animals is that they feel things in gross. The kitten who learned to respond differently to the signals, "I must feed those cats" and "I will not feed them," felt each signal as a vague total, including the tone, the movements of my head, etc. It did not have an idea of the sound of *I*, another of the sound of *must*, another of the sound *feed*, etc. It did not turn the complex impression into a set of elements, but felt it, as I have said, in gross. The dog that learned to get out of a box by pulling a loop of wire did not feel the parts of the box separately, the bolt as a definite circle of a certain size, did not feel his act as a sum of certain particular movements. The monkey who learned to know the letter K from the letter Y did not feel the separate lines of the letter, have definite ideas of the parts. He just felt one way when he saw one total impression and another way when he saw another.

Strictly human thinking, on the contrary, has as its essential characteristic the breaking up of gross total situations into feelings of particular facts. When in the presence of ten jumping tigers we not only feel like running, but also feel the number of tigers, their color, their size, etc. When, instead of merely associating some act with some situation in the animal way, we think the situation out, we have a set of particular feelings of its elements. In some cases, it is true, we remain restricted to the animal sort of feelings. The sense impressions of suffocation, of the feeling of a new style of clothes, of the pressure of 10 feet of water above us, of malaise, of nausea and such like remain for most of us vague total feelings to which we react and which we feel most acutely but which do not take the form of definite ideas that we can isolate or combine or compare. Such feelings we say are not parts of our real intellectual life. They *are* parts of our intellectual life if we mean by it the mental life concerned in learning, but they are not if we mean by it the life of reasoning.

Can we now see how the vague gross feelings of the animal sort might turn into the well-defined particular ideas of the human sort, by the aid of a multitude of delicate associations?

It seems to be a general law of mind that any mental element which occurs with a number of different mental elements, appears, that is, in a number of different combinations, tends to thereby acquire an independent life of its own. We show children six lines, six dots, six peas, six pieces of paper, etc., and thus create the definite feeling of sixness. Out of the gross feelings of a certain number of lines, of dots, etc., we evolve the definite elementary feeling of sixness by making the 'six' aspect of the situations appear in a number of different connections. We learn to feel whiteness as a definite idea by seeing white paper, white cloth, white eggs, white plates, etc. We learn to feel the meaning of *but* or *in* or *notwithstanding* by feeling the meanings of many total phrases containing each of them. Now in this general law by which different associates for the same elementary process elevate it out of its position as an undifferentiated fragment of a gross total feeling, we have, I think, the manner in which the vague feelings of the nine-months-old infant become the definite ideas of the five-year-old boy, the manner in which in the race the animal mind has evolved into the human, and the explanation of the service performed by the increase in the delicacy of structure of the human brain and the consequent increase in the number of associations.

The bottle to the six-months-old infant is a vague sense-impression which the infant does not think about or indeed in the common meanings of the words perceive or remember or imagine. Its presence does not arouse ideas, but action. It is not to him a thing so big, or so shaped, or so heavy, but is just a vaguely sizable thing to be reached for, grabbed and sucked. Like the lower animals, with the exception that as he grows a little older he reacts in very many more ways, the child feels things in gross in a way to lead to direct reactions. Vague sense-impressions and impulses make up his mental life. The bottle, which to a dog would be a thing to smell at and paw, to a kitten a thing to smell at and perhaps worry, is to the child a little later a thing to grab and suck and turn over and drop and pick up and pull at and finger and rub against its toes and so on. The sight of the bottle thus becomes associated with many different reactions, and thus by our general law tends to gain a position independent of any of them, to evolve from the condition of being a portion of the cycles see-grab, see-drop, see-turn over, etc., to the condition of being a definite idea.

The increased delicacy and complexity of the cell structures in the human brain give the possibility of very small parts of the brain-processes forming different connections, allow the brain to work in very great detail, provide processes ready to be turned into definite ideas. The great number of associations which the human being forms furnish the means by which this last event is consummated. The infant's vague feelings of total situations are by virtue of the detailed working of his brain all ready to split up into parts, and his general activity and curiosity provide the multitude of different connections which allow them to do so. The dog, on the other hand, has few or no ideas because his brain acts in coarse fashion and because there are few connections with each single process.

When once the mind begins to function by having definite ideas, all the phenomena of reasoning soon appear. The transition from one idea to another is the feeling of their relationship, of similarity or difference or whatever it may be. As soon as we find any words or other symbols to express such a feeling, or to express our idea of an action or condition, we have explicit judgments. Observation of any child will show us that the mind cannot rest in a condition where it has a large body of ideas without comparing them and thinking about them. The ideas carry within them the forces that make abstractions, feelings of similarity, judgments and other characteristics of reasoning.

In children two and three years of age we find all these elements of reasoning present and functioning. The product of children's reasoning is often irrational, but the processes are all there. The following instances from a collection of children's sayings by Mr. H. W. Brown show children making inductions and deductions after the same general fashion as adults : —

(2 yrs.) T. pulled the hairs on his father's wrist. Father. "Don't, T., you hurt papa !" T. "It didn't hurt grandpa."

(2 yrs. 5 mos.) M. said, "Gracie can't walk, she wears little bits of shoes; if she had mine, she could walk. When I get some new ones, I'm going to give her these, so she can walk."

(2 yrs. 9 mos.) He usually has a nap in the forenoon, but Friday he did not seem sleepy, so his mother did not put him to bed. Before long he began to say, "Bolly's sleepy; mamma put him in the crib !" This he said very pleasantly at first; but, as she paid no attention to him, he said, "Bolly cry, then mamma will." And he sat down on the floor and roared.

(3 yrs.) It was between five and six in the afternoon; the mother was getting the baby asleep. J. had no one to play with. He kept saying, "I wish R. would come home; mamma, put baby to bed, so R. will come home." I usually get home about six, and as the baby is put to bed about half-past five, he had associated the one with the other.

(3 yrs.) W. likes to play with oil paints. Two days ago my father told W. he must not touch the paints any more, for he was too small. This morning W. said, "When my papa is a very old man, and when I am a big man and don't need any papa, then I can paint, can't I, mamma?"

(3 yrs.) G.'s aunt gave him ten cents. G. went out, but soon came back saying, "Mamma, we will be rich now." "Why so,

G. ?" "Because I planted my ten cents, and we will have lots of ten cents growing."

(3 yrs.) B. climbed up into a large express wagon, and would not get out. I helped him out, and it was not a minute before he was back in the wagon. I said, "B., how are you going to get out of there now?" He replied, "I can stay here till it gets little, and then I can get out my own self."

(3 yrs.) F. is not allowed to go to the table to eat unless she has her face and hands washed and her hair combed. The other day she went to a lady visiting at her house and said, "Please wash my face and hands and comb my hair; I am very hungry."

(3 yrs.) If C. is told not to touch a certain thing, that it will bite him, he always asks if it has a mouth. The other day he was examining a plant, to see if it had a mouth. He was told not to break it, and he said, "Oh, it won't bite, because I can't find any mouth."

Nowhere in the animal kingdom do we find the psychological elements of reasoning save where there is a mental life made up of the definite feelings which I have called 'ideas,' but they spring up like magic as soon as we get in a child a body of such ideas. If we have traced satisfactorily the evolution of a life of ideas from the animal life of vague sense-impressions and impulses, we may be reasonably sure that no difficulty awaits us in following the life of ideas in its course from the chaotic dream of early childhood to the logical world-view of the adult scientist.

In a very short time we have come a long way, from the simple learning of the minnow or chick to the science and logic of man. The general frame of mind which one acquires from the study of animal behavior and of the mental development of young children makes our hypothesis seem vital and probable. If the facts did eventually corroborate it, we should have an eminently simple genesis of human faculty, for we could put together the gist of our contention in a few words. We should say : —

"The function of intellect is to provide a means of modifying our reactions to the circumstances of life, so that we may secure pleasure, the symptom of welfare. Its general law is that when in a certain situation an animal acts so that pleasure results, that act is selected from all those performed and associated with that situation, so that, when the situation recurs, the act will be more likely to follow than it was before ; that on the contrary the acts which, when performed in a certain situation, have brought discomfort, tend to be dissociated from that situation. The intellectual evolution of the race consists in an increase in the number, delicacy, complexity, permanence and speed of formation of such associations. In man this increase reaches such a point that an apparently new type of mind results, which conceals the real continuity of the process. This mental evolution parallels the evolution of the cell structures of the brain from few and simple and gross to many and complex and delicate."

Nowhere more truly than in his mental capacities is man a part of nature. His instincts, that is, his inborn tendencies to feel and act in certain ways, show throughout marks of kinship with the lower animals, especially with our nearest relatives physically, the monkeys. His sense-powers show no new creation. His intellect we have seen to be a simple though extended variation from the general animal sort. This again is presaged by the similar variation in the case of the monkeys. Amongst the minds of animals that of man leads, not as a demigod from another planet, but as a king from the same race.

INDEX

Abstraction, 120. *See also* Reasoning.
Action-system, importance of the study of the, 15 f.; of monkeys, 190 f., 237.
Anecdotal school in animal psychology, 23 ff., 151 f.
Apparatus, descriptions of, 29 ff., 56 ff., 61 f., 169 f., 177 ff., 196 ff.
Assimilation, 249 f.
Association, as a problem in animal psychology, 20 ff.; by similarity, 116 ff.; complexity of, 132 ff.; conditions of, 43 ff.; delicacy of, 128 ff., 195 ff.; development of, in the animal kingdom, 285 ff.; in cats, 38 ff.; in chicks, 63 f.; in dogs, 56 ff.; in fishes, 169 ff.; in man, 123 ff., 127, 285; in monkeys, 182 ff., 194 f., 209 ff.; in relation to attention, 44 ff.; to individual differences, 52 ff.; to inhibition, 142 ff.; to instincts, 36 f., 142 ff.; to previous experience, 48 ff.; number of connections formed by, 135 ff.; permanence of connections formed by, 138 ff., 194 f., 203 f.; progress of, measurable by time-curves, 28, 40, 42; the mental fact in, 98 ff.; without ideas, 101 f., 127, 209 ff. *See also* Associations and Learning.
Associations, complexity, 132 ff.; delicacy, 128 ff., 195 ff.; number, 121, 135 ff.; permanence, 138 ff., 194 f., 203 f.
Associative memory. *See* Association.
Attention, 144 ff.; and association, 44 ff.; to imposed movements, 103 ff.

Behavior, acquired tendencies to, 244 ff. (*see also* Association); evolution of, 272 ff.; general laws of, 241 ff.; indefiniteness of the term, 5; of cats, 35 ff., 88 f., and *passim;* of chicks, 63 f., 138, 143 f., 156 ff., and *passim;* of dogs, 59 ff., 92 ff.; of fishes, 169 ff.; of monkeys, 182 ff.; original tendencies to, 242 f. (*see also* Instincts); predictability of, 241 f.; proposed simplification of the laws of, 265 ff.;

versus consciousness as an object of study, 1 ff. *See also* Association, Instincts, Learning, Memory, etc.
Bosworth, F. D., 240.

Cats, associative processes in, 35 ff.; imitation in, 85 ff.; the presence of ideas in, 100 ff.; reasoning in, 67 ff.
Chicks, associative processes in, 61 ff.; imitation in, 81 ff.; instincts of, 156 ff.
Complexity, of associations, 132 ff.
Concepts, 116 ff.
Connection-systems, action of, in association, 246 ff., 266; importance of the study of, 16 f.
Consciousness, amenability of, to scientific study, 7 ff.; as pure experience, 13 f.; as studied by the one who has or is it, 10 ff.; of animals, 25 f., 67 ff., 98 ff., 123, 146 f., and *passim;* social, 146 f.; space-relations of, 14; *versus* behavior as an object of study, 1 ff.
Coördinations, of chicks, 160 ff.

Dean, B., 161.
Delicacy of association, 128 ff., 195 ff.
Dewey, J., 6.
Differences, between species of animals in the associative processes, 64 ff.
Discomfort, as an influence in learning, 245 ff.
Discrimination, in cats and dogs, 128 ff.; in chicks, 156 ff.; in monkeys, 195 ff.
Dogs, associative processes in, 56 ff.; imitation in, 91 ff.; the presence of ideas in, 115 f.; reasoning in, 67 ff.

Education, applications of animal psychology in, 149 f.
Effect, the law of, 244 f., 266 ff.
Emotional reactions of chicks, 162 ff.
Evolution, of behavior, 272 ff.; of human intellect, 282 ff.; of ideas, 289 ff.
Exercise, the law of, 244 f.
Experience, the influence of previous, 48 ff.

295